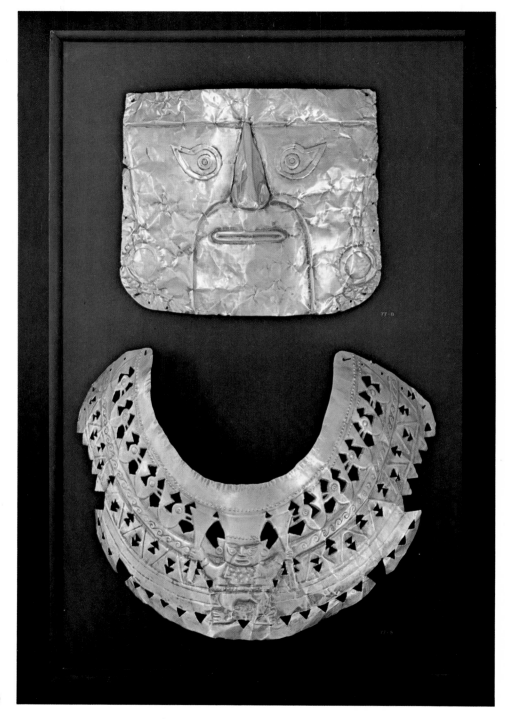

CHIMU MASK AND PECTORAL (CATALOG NOS. 77-8, 77-9)

MAN CAME THIS WAY

Objects from The Phil Berg Collection

Catalog and Commentary by Phil Berg

LOS ANGELES COUNTY MUSEUM OF ART · March 9 - May 30, 1971

COVER ILLUSTRATION:

Enlarged clay impression of archaic cylinder seal, Sumer-Akkadian,
ca. 3000-2700 B.C. Depicted is a celestial court scene: the mischievous
god Zu, flanked by guards, stands before the supreme god, Ea,
presumably to be judged for one of his frequent misdemeanors.
(See catalog entry 8-c.)

FRONTISPIECE ILLUSTRATION:

Chimu gold mask and pectoral, from Peru (Chan Chan area),
ca. 1300-1438. (See catalog entries 77-8, 77-9.)

PREFACE

Increasingly we are aware that the history of art is actually the history of man. The surviving arts of man—whether cave paintings at Altamira or Luristan bronzes—communicate the hopes, the fears, and the joys of the human experience across vast chasms of time.

The Phil Berg Collection, by its broad and eclectic nature, and with its emphasis on the more ancient works of man, is a splendid example of a collection that teaches the history of man. The Museum is grateful to Mr. and Mrs. Berg for their munificent gift of much of the Collection, and for this first opportunity—since announcement of the gift—to share the objects, by means of an exhibition, with the Museum's large membership and its still larger public audience. Coincident with the exhibition, the Museum is pleased to publish Mr. Berg's own catalog of that part of the Collection now deeded over to the Museum. The commentary, a majority of the photographs, all of the object descriptions and attributions are by the collector himself. Both the catalog and the exhibited works are testament to Mr. Berg's diligence, collecting zeal, and unending interest in the creativity and diversity of Man.

Our colleagues in the profession, and indeed all who are believers in museums as vital, educational institutions, should know that Mr. Berg's gift is unique and important in several respects. First, it provides a broad base, especially in the area of ancient art, for the Museum's careful development of a meaningful Near Eastern collection. Secondly, a most generous gesture by Mr. Berg will permit the Museum to augment his Collection by means of a special fund that accompanies his gift, or through the exchange or sale of works now in the presentation group—provided only that new works thus obtained are of greater quality or significance and that they were created before the XVI century.

There is a third factor that means a great deal to me, personally, both as a former university chancellor and as a museum president. Art museums have leaned rather heavily in the past to letting works of art speak for themselves. There are indeed whole schools of curators who dread the common label, who feel that art requires little explanation. But we face a new and hungry audience of museum goers today. Indeed it has been observed that modern art museums are, properly, colleges without entrance requirements. The Phil Berg Collection is truly a cross-cultural study collection. Its many works —installed as in the present exhibition with supportive maps and photomurals, chronological charts, and detailed labels—will help the Museum to reach a greater number of fellow citizens of all ages and backgrounds who come, not to be baffled and overwhelmed, but to be inspired, to learn, to enjoy, and to appreciate the creative genius existing in many cultures throughout time.

It is appropriate that the Los Angeles County Museum of Art will have custody of more than four hundred objects from The Phil Berg Collection. Mr. Berg has long been identified with the community, and with the motion picture industry in particular. That the Hollywood of Clark Gable, Judy Garland, Wallace Beery, Charles Laughton, and scores of other stars and directors whose careers were developed or managed by Phil Berg should now appear in the Museum in the form of Sumerian worshipper figures and Chinese bronzes is a distinctly happy and welcome development. The Trustees and staff, and, I am certain, our Members also, and scores of thousands of Museum visitors join me in this warm acknowledgment of our considerable indebtedness to Phil and Leila Berg. Their gift will open the eyes of many.

FRANKLIN D. MURPHY
President
Los Angeles County Museum of Art

FOREWORD

It is hoped that what is attempted here forms a comprehensible pattern. Every age has good and bad artists. Every collection reflects the personal taste of the collector. Accordingly, we start with a few examples of artifacts from the dawn of civilization, over five thousand years ago, and continue into the modern world. Although much is archaeological, we trust that the aesthetic achievements of all these peoples through the millennia are discernible. There is profound history even in the human face as depicted over the ages: petrified in the ancient Orient, it manages a frozen archaic smile amongst the Egyptians and the Greeks; harsh in Rome, wooden in the Dark Ages, it becomes worldly in the XVIII century, and then sadly retreats into solitude today. But we are actually not spatially separated from our forebears. The frequently beautiful objects which follow are neither bizarre curios nor heathen abominations. They are part of our heritage and should command our interest.

For orientation this compilation is divided into seven sections.

1. *Mesopotamia, The Levant, and Egypt.* (Pages 6 to 39). Mesopotamia was the "cradle of civilization," and The Levant was the land bridge over which the diverse Oriental cultures first travelled to our western world. Egypt must be included here as it was almost contemporary and shortly thereafter became an integral part of the initial pattern.

2. *Greece, Rome, and the West.* (Pages 40 to 67). Our Occidental culture, philosophy, ethics, and art deviated from the Near Eastern orientalized concepts in the Aegean and Grecian cultures, were copied by Rome, and were disseminated through Europe to all the world.

3. *The Orient.* (Pages 68 to 93). High Far Eastern cultures, nascent about one thousand years later than those of Mesopotamia, evolved independently of ours and have not, until comparatively recently, markedly influenced western civilization.

4. *Oceania and the Pacific Basin.* (Pages 94 to 103). The peoples of the Islands of the Pacific, Malaysia, and our Pacific Northwest Coast (arbitrarily included as part of the Pacific Basin) had a cosmic vital thrust that found an outlet in music and the dance, oratory and ceremony. Sculpture, carvings, and masks expressed their unity with nature.

5. *The Pre-Columbian Americas.* (Pages 105 to 172). Here arose a great civilization virtually without extra-continental communication after the initial migrations. The first impact of its art in Europe four and a half centuries ago caused the great German master, Albrecht Dürer, to huzza: "I have seen the things brought to the King from the new golden land—wondrous things much more beautiful to behold than miracles—I have seen therein wonders of Art." Today, at last, he has found sympathetic ears.

6. *Negro Africa.* (Pages 173 to 183). This section includes only aboriginal Negro Africa as North Africa, especially Egypt, has closer ties with Mediterranean antiquity. From Negro Africa came the first recognized "primitives," acknowledged revelations, influencing so many artists for these past six decades.

7. *And To Today.* (Pages 185 to 207). Here we are in the last few hundred years until today. Recent developments demand a "no comment" here. A later amplification of our dissent guarantees augmentation of your obfuscation.

Each section is preceded by a short, possibly oversimplified explanation, as we follow the concatenation of history succinctly, maps for orientation, and, where applicable, synoptic chronologies so that evolution may be easily traced. Copying from one book is called plagiarism—from many books, research. Credit and our thanks to the scholars whose writings we have "researched." These are listed in the bibliography, which also suggests further informative, interesting, non-technical reading for each area.

The maps are all our originals. Of the 384 photographs herein, the eight color plates and all of the gold and jade illustrations were photographed by Edward Cornachio and John Gebhart, official

Museum photographers. The blurry balance, easily distinguishable, is by the Bergs.

I express profound thanks to my wife, Leila, whose understanding participation has made our frequently demanding pattern of life possible; to our dear friend, that distinguished scholar Dr. Karl With, Professor Emeritus, University of California at Los Angeles, for his invaluable help and suggestions in the preparation of this book; and to the erudite Deputy Director of the Los Angeles County Museum of Art, Rexford Stead, whose warm rapport and enthusiasm for art of the ancient world encouraged our gift to the Museum. Our sincere gratitude, also, to our friend Michael Morrison who, possessed of nonpareil inspiration, unselfishly contributed his talent for the design of this exhibition.

The lure of collecting has been all-engrossing. It has entailed archaeological expeditions to many lands. The acquisition of a single object has frequently been the result of thousands of miles of travel, which has taken us to almost every country in the world. There have been long, fruitless journeys tracking down rumors. There has been endless intrigue. But it has all been rewarding. Most important, this is "collecting for learning."

PHIL BERG

"Savitar,"
Bel-Air, California
December 1970

SUMERIAN WORSHIPPER FIGURE (CATALOG NO. 4.)

SECTION I. MESOPOTAMIA, THE LEVANT, AND EGYPT

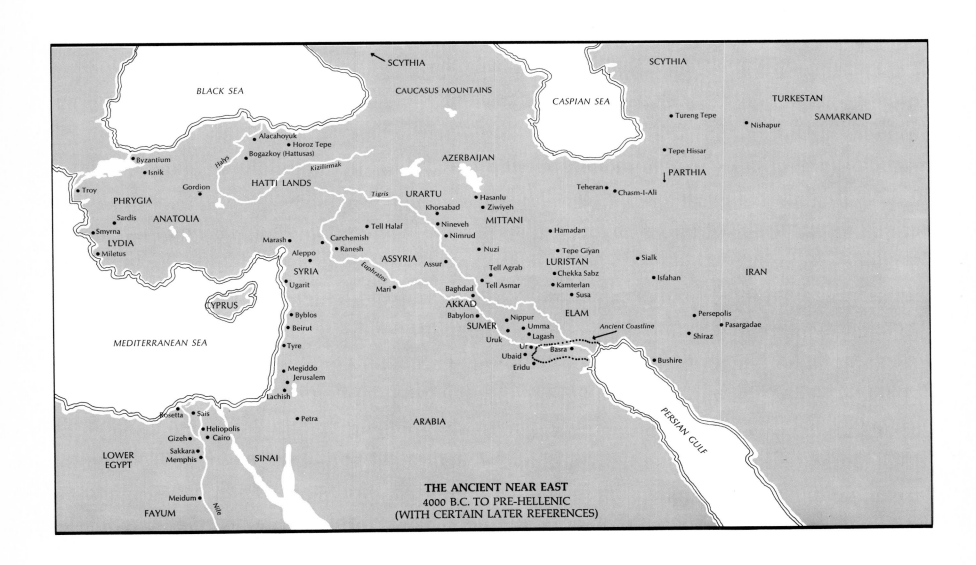

THE ANCIENT NEAR EAST
4000 B.C. TO PRE-HELLENIC
(WITH CERTAIN LATER REFERENCES)

Why should one be interested in a remote region of western Asia between the lower Tigris and Euphrates Rivers, the heart of the Fertile Crescent? This Plain of Shinar was rendered prolific in ancient times by a fabulous system of man-made canals. This "cradle of civilization" saw the rise of city-states older than dynastic Egypt—Sumer, Eridu, Ur, Lagash, Akkad, Babylon, and others. Over six thousand years ago, the proto-Sumerians had here evolved mankind's first notable culture, based upon agriculture with canal irrigation. Pottery and metal work were made into fine arts, and cuneiform (wedge-shaped) writing (See Nos. 2a, b) here originated. The wheel first appeared. Laws were codified. Well-planned palaces and temples, although of mud brick, as the valley lacked stone, had been built. Archaeological excavations by Winckelmann, Botta, Childe, Woolley, Speiser, and others confirm this.

Then trade appeared. For what is known as "urban" civilization is always essentially commercial. Primarily the town is a stronghold and a market. But commerce was born in spoliation. Hermes is the patron divinity of both brigandage and trade. As we trace history, we recognize that it is the tale of man's cupidity for trade routes and the wealth of neighbors. Coleridge observed:

> A wild and dream-like trade of blood and guile
> Too foolish for a tear, too wicked for a smile.

Consider the rest of the world in the year 4000 B.C. when Sumer had achieved this development. Mohenjo-Daro, India's first known urban culture, born in the Indus Valley, was not to flower for almost a thousand years. The oldest records in China date from the Shang Dynasty, 1766 B.C. Aborigines sparsely populated the continent of Europe and western Asia. Africa and the Americas were in primeval barbarism. Egypt was still in the late Neolithic Age, although possessed of a generative culture.

To start at our beginnings, these *Sumerians* were a non-Semitic people and lived in the Land of the Two Rivers, the Tigris and the Euphrates. They were short, with globular heads and eagle beaks. Their wealthy city-states engaged in endless, enervating internecine warfare. They rivaled the Semitic cities to their north in Babylonia, and ultimately Sargon (Sharrukin, who reigned 2334-2279 B.C.) assimilated them, and they were incorporated into the *Akkadian* empire. But the Sumerian culture persisted (Nos. 3, 4).* A few

hundred years later Sumer briefly revived (III Dynasty of Ur), only to die as a nation before the rise of Elam (No. 9) and the resurgent power of Babylonia. This has always been the pattern of man's history. The conqueror has either had the new weapon—metal, the horse, the chariot, the phalanx, gunpowder, the bomb—or has been the vigorous barbarian. The conquered is either assimilated or assimilates, and fortunately, the higher culture generally survives, with infusion of new blood.

With the ascendancy of the Akkadians was inaugurated what the great James Henry Breasted described as *The Semitic World*. From the remotest ages, a group of primarily pastoral peoples of white stock, called Semites, divided into many tribes, none of which ever long united into one coherent nation, ranged the deserts of Arabia. They all spoke and still speak dialects of the Semitic tongue. Prior to 3000 B.C. they had founded walled towns on the western end of the Fertile Crescent. There were other groups of these one-time desert wanderers flourishing in what are now the Levant States. Of those Semites who settled to the north and east, we have already met the Akkadians. Hence, you see, the Semites invaded the Fertile Crescent from the inside of the semi-circle. We shall see that they prevailed for over two millennia. The non-Semites, different groups of the white race from the highland zone to the north and to the Zagros Mountains, were occluded for this epoch.

Suzerainty over this world, after an initial confluence, was maintained by three principal powers, whose ambitions repeatedly conflicted—*Egypt*, Mesopotamia's *Babylonian* and *Assyrian Empires*, and the *Hittites* of Anatolia. These Hittites were Indo-European, but they enter the scene late, and they survived as a nation for only about six hundred years. So, here lived a preponderately Semitic linguistic family group including Babylonians, Assyrians, Canaanites, Moabites, Phoenicians, Hebrews, and Aramaeans, and the Arabic and Ethiopian groups. Here too, were the Hamito-Semites of Egypt and the progenitors of North Africa's modern Berbers, Tauregs, Riffs, and Algerians. Note that the Hebrews are only a small division of the Semites. A truly conglomerate family! Now we shall examine the erstwhile big three.

Numbers in parentheses refer to illustrations of objects which follow each section of text.

The River Nile is the nucleus of *Egypt*. Away from the river all is desert. The Nile's yearly rich alluvial inundations fertilize the valley and the delta. The demarcation point between Upper and Lower Egypt is just south of Cairo. It is Egypt's good fortune that the Nile current carries her commerce to the Mediterranean, and the prevailing north wind carries it up river. But the mighty Nile is no tranquil stream. Its flow requires control to avoid alternating periods of devastating flood and drought. To mitigate the capricious moods of the waters and the heavens, great works had to be constructed which imposed a discipline upon the inhabitants and required communal organization. A socialistic monarchy arose in Egypt in the early third millennium. To find its like we must go to the empire of the Incas or to the U.S.S.R. of today. The Pharaoh (this word originally meant "Great House" and only later designated the ruler) was absolute sovereign and monopolistic land owner. Private property was unknown, and every Egyptian was a civil servant incorporated into an immense hierarchy of bureaucratic administration. To this mobilization of the population can be credited Egypt's Pyramid Age, which lasted over five hundred years, until the incredible pyramid line exceeded sixty miles.

Archaeology cannot yet accurately trace the variegated pre-dynastic history of Egypt. It appears that there were at least two unions of Upper and Lower Egypt prior to the founding of the First Dynasty around 3200 B.C. by Menes, who centralized the government. However, the plow had already supplanted the hoe in Egypt, and the country had surplus portable wealth—grain—which fostered foreign trade. Architecture, mathematics, astronomy, hieroglyphs (picture writing, see No. 39), political cohesion, and other facets of man's dawning civilization advanced. Complex and contradictory gods were worshipped, including a pantheon of animal divinities, the Sun (Ra), the Nile (Osiris), and fecundity (Isis). During the times of Menes, copper, on a large scale, from Sinai, inaugurated Egypt's Age of Metal. Diodorus tells us that standards of living reached a new peak. Many Egyptian artifacts survive as they resist time in dry Egypt, which has been a mecca for archaeologists from Mariette and Petrie until today. Napoleon inaugurated Egyptian archaeology with his savants, and Champollion unlocked the key to its lore when he deciphered the Rosetta stone.

Through the annals of the thirty dynasties we now may follow Egypt's intervals of greatness as well as of anarchy, civil war, foreign invasion, and general political and cultural disruption, which have been somewhat arbitrarily called the "Intermediate Periods." Witness Hyksos, Ethiopian, Assyrian, Persian, and lesser dominations, conquest by Alexander the Great, followed by the three-century rule of his general Ptolemy and his descendants. Egypt became a Roman province and later, with the collapse of the Roman Empire, came under the rule of the Byzantine emperors until they were overrun by the Arabs in A.D. 640. Toynbee regards the history of Egypt as a great creation followed by tenacious millennia of decline, rather than the usual picture of a series of equally interesting "periods." Yes, Egypt enjoyed its highly cultivated periods of great progress, notably the period of Empire, but the hated foreigner, even to the Englishman, persistently prevailed.

The salient characteristic of Egyptian art (Nos. 37 to 59) is a combination of geometric regularity and a keen observation of nature. It is concerned only with essentials and achieves its power by concentration on basic form. It impresses us as life-like, yet is remote and enduring. While largely funerary, it is not funereal. The lugubrious accent often placed upon it is preposterous. Although it is true that most surviving material exists only because it happened to have been placed in the tombs of the dead, it reflects not a preoccupation with death but rather the intense interest in life characteristic of an industrious people. Egypt's later Ptolemaic, Roman, and Coptic expressions (Nos. 55-59) are, of course, deviant.

To return to Mesopotamia, as the Sumero-Akkadian people lost their vigor, other Semites, the *Amorites*, at about 2100 B.C. erupted from a small town upriver, named Babylon, on the Plain of Shinar, which henceforth we may properly call *Babylonia*. Within a century they had become masters of all, under their great legislator-king, Hammurabi (reigned 1792-1750 B.C.), the promulgator of civil, procedural, criminal (eye for an eye), and commercial codes. These contain much from which we might profit today. The state became no more than a referee and regulator, and, in contrast to chaotic, socialistic Egypt, private property was formally recognized, and individual enterprise with all the machinery of capitalistic trading was initiated. Commercial interest, even in religion, became the prevalent influence, and the people prospered. Works of art from Hammurabi's period are scarce, but they display a fine dignity and

EGYPTIAN SYNOPTIC CHRONOLOGICAL TABLE			
Byzantine Period	395-640 A.D.	Second Intermediate Period (XIII-XVII Dynasty) (Hyksos)	1780-1546 B.C.
Roman Period (Start Coptic-Christian)	30 B.C.-395 A.D.	Middle Kingdom (XI-XII Dynasty)	2000-1780 B.C.
Ptolemaic Period	332-30 B.C.	First Intermediate Period (VII-X Dynasty)	2250-2000 B.C.
Late Dynastic (XXII-XXX Dynasty) (Saite Period, XXVI Dynasty, 663-525 B.C.)	1085-663 B.C.	Old Kingdom (III-VI Dynasty)	2800-2250 B.C.
New Kingdom (XVIII-XXI Dynasty) (Empire 1567-1090 B.C.)	1546-1085 B.C.	Archaic Period (I-II Dynasty)	3200-2800 B.C.

impressiveness (No. 10). Babylonian sculptured reliefs set Near East style for succeeding centuries. The representation of human form, however, was muffled under heavy garments. Portraiture was indistinguishable of likeness. But the beautiful art of seal cutting attained a zenith (Nos. 8a, b, and c).

The first splendidly organized Babylonian Empire barely survived three hundred years—but remember that these United States have existed less than two hundred. Then Babylonia was invaded by savage, also Semitic, *Kassite* nomads from the east. Then the *Hittites* advanced out of the northwest, Anatolia, and captured Babylon. Theirs was only a hurried raid for plunder, but when they withdrew in about 1750 B.C., they left the country to Kassite domination, and Babylonian civilization lapsed into stagnation, concluding its first great chapter. Babylonian hegemony over western Asia was lost.

Again, to the north of Babylon, the land of *Assur*, which later gave its name to *Assyria*, had been constantly beset by predatory neighbors. Thus obligated and toughened by the strain of unceasing warfare, the Assyrian kings created a powerful military state. Early a merchant class had brought wealth to the young nation. This emergent power coveted the metals found to the west and access to the Mediterranean for ascendancy over western Asia. We shall soon see how Assyria fulfilled its ambitions.

Shortly we shall more fully discuss the Indo-Europeans. However,

by 1500 B.C. an advance guard of these people, called *Mittani*, horsemen from the northern grasslands, maintained their state on the Euphrates. The terrible chariots of their horse-breeding aristocracy had even entered Assyria and held the country subject for a time. And there was the other Indo-European salient, the great Hittite Empire.

The *Hittites*, whom we have called one of the big three in the ancient Near East, are surprisingly depreciated by historians. Their civilization was comparable to Babylonia and Egypt. We have mentioned their brief subjugation of Babylon. Hittites made vassals of the kings of Syria and Palestine and faced Egypt as an equal and powerful rival for many years. Modern knowledge of them really only goes back to Knudtzon's discoveries in 1902. The deciphering of the Amarna tablets at this time was the earliest historical evidence of the penetration of the Near East by these Indo-European settlers. No one is sure from whence the Hittites originally came. They adopted the indigenous civilization of eastern Anatolia and developed it. But they long remained totally distinct from the neighboring Babylonians in their beliefs, ideas, and customs. They possessed their own style of monumental sculpture, ornamentation, and dress. The writings of their rulers show moderation and wisdom. We have stayed at Bogazkoy, the site of the fortress Hattusas and its citadel Buyukkal, a most spectacular architectural achievement, with its walls and buildings integrated with the rugged crags of the ravine. This city is probably the Indo-European prototype of all European fortified towns. Alaca Hüyük has almost disappeared (Nos. 12, 13). Men like Winckler, Bittle, Gurney, and others have partly illuminated the Hittites. The Hatti lands of Suppiluliumas were not the home of "obscure and tiresome little tribes of Biblical Bedouins," but of a powerful empire, short lived.

Another intrusion in the Near East after the XVI century B.C. was commercial and political. New infiltrations of Semitic *Aramaeans*, principally in Syria and to the south in Palestine, appeared. Although they were not organized into a single nation, they became the great commercial leaders of their age. The Aramaeans were a highly civilized people and carried their language, called Aramaic, with them (No. 6). Aramaic became the language of the entire Fertile Crescent and even displaced its similar sister tongue, Hebrew. Centuries later this merchant tongue was still spoken by Jesus and the other Hebrews.

So the aspiring rulers of *Assyria* gazed out upon a hostile foreground of Mittani, Aramaeans, and Phoenicians while in the background were the two great powers—the Egyptians to the southwest and the Hittites to the northwest. Then Assyria witnessed a tremendous struggle for supremacy between Egypt and the Hittite Empire. Mittani, through unfortunate alliances, was obliterated. The Hittites were invaded from behind by Phrygia and Thracia and were annihilated. The Empire of Egypt collapsed. Finally all combatants were exhausted by their protracted, inconclusive wars. Thus by 1150 B.C., Assyria inherited the Empire of the East by default. However, the Aramaean kings of Damascus, the Phoenicians, and the Hebrew kingdoms united to deny the Assyrians permanent access to the Mediterranean for another three hundred years.

The Iron Age had been initiated by the Hittites, who had started to fashion and distribute the metal at about 1300 B.C. Evidently the Assyrians later stock-piled it, as a single arsenal room of Sargon II's palace was found to contain about two hundred tons of iron implements. Several centuries passed while the Assyrians consolidated their eastern position after they had conquered and razed Babylon. Then they fielded the first large armies equipped with weapons of iron and the battering ram. They were now invincible. Under merciless Sargon II (No. 20) and Sennacherib, their pillagings, burnings,

and massacres form one of the bloodiest periods of the history of mankind. The end of the Bronze Age marked throughout the entire ancient world an eclipse of civilization which was to last for hundreds of years. Assyrian devastations and the barbarian invasions of Greece (to be discussed in Section II) desolated the ancient world. Until after 700 B.C. the ferocious Assyrians engulfed the Fertile Crescent and the eastern Mediterranean, and their megalomania led to the conquest of Egypt. With the plunder and tribute from conquered lands, Assyrian kings built magnificent Nineveh and Nimrud (Calah). Their vast palaces were decorated with alabaster reliefs proclaiming the despots' omnipotence (Nos. 1, 2, 2a, 2b). Their impressive triple arches, the ancestor of the Roman triumphal arch, were flanked by huge alabaster human-headed bulls and faced with glazed brick in gorgeous colors. It is indicative, though, that their sculpture treated only of battle and the hunt and was more successful in the rendering of animals than men. Assyrian civilization was more bloodthirsty than creative.

The unceasing wars led to the destruction of the industrial and wealth-producing population, both at home and throughout the conquered countries. The peasants were permanently taken from the land for the armies. Assyria contained the seeds of its own death and suddenly, dramatically, collapsed internally. In the voice of the Hebrew prophet Nahum we hear an echo of the exulting hosanna which resounded from the Caspian to the Nile as the nations discovered that the scourge of the east had at last been laid low. The ancient world emerged from a long Dark Age.

Another Semitic people, Babylonian kinsmen, the *Chaldeans*, took mighty Nineveh. Under their Nebuchadnezzar, Babylon was rebuilt with the addition of the famous hanging gardens of legendary Queen Semiramis. The Chaldean, or Second Babylonian Empire, is notable for its opulence (No. 11), brevity (seventy-four years), its contribution to the start of astronomical observations, and the destruction of Jerusalem. However, before the eclipse of the Semitic World we must consider two other peoples who have contributed incalculably to our western heritage—the *Hebrews* and the *Phoenicians*.

Modern archaeology is constantly furnishing new proofs for much of the historical authenticity of the Old Testament. Abraham, son of Terah, described in Genesis as "the Hebrew," came to Canaan with his wives, his people, and his flocks in about 1900 B.C. But unfortunately Abraham's nomads settled in a periodically unproductive land, subject to famine, and already peopled by *Canaanites*, their congeners. It is interesting to note that the prominent aquiline nose, still considered to be the mark of the Semite, especially of the Jew, was acquired here by intermarriage with the non-Semitic early Anatolians.

Under Jacob, surnamed *Israel*, the already persecuted "chosen people" departed Canaan for Egypt to improve their lot and were taken into captivity. Then, about 1300 B.C., led out of Egypt by Moses, they returned to Canaan. But Palestine, straitened between sea and desert, is a prolongation of the land bridge between Asia and Africa. You should see the ruins of the fortress of Megiddo, on the Plain of Esdraelon. Excavations have uncovered, in strata, the ramparts of over twenty former civilizations, holders of this pass, from antiquity to Allenby. The Hebrews ultimately settled here after fighting the Canaanites, the Moabites, and the Philistines for their lands (Nos. 18, 19). At this crossroad there was no prospect for freedom from foreign aggression. The Jews were dogged by misfortune, split by schism that set Israel against Judah, Shechem against Jerusalem. They bred murders and palace revolutions. Assyria deported the Hebrew inhabitants of Samaria. Babylonia took the Judaeans into captivity. Later, after 550 B.C., thanks to the wise, tolerant Persian, Cyrus the Great, the Jews were permitted to return to Palestine, only to again come under the domination of foreign conquerors—Macedonians, Syrians, and finally Romans. They revolted in vain. Their temple was destroyed, and the people of Israel dispersed. In every country, the individual Jew resumed his destiny as a wanderer. But they taught the truth of monotheism to the world. Their gift to mankind was the concept of a universal God, a just God. Their saga is indubitably the acme of man's survival in the face of adversity. Possibly their very vicissitudes predicated their continuity in contrast to their more powerful contemporaries' evanescence. Jesus, the world's greatest teacher, was of the Hebrews.

Homer, in the *Odyssey*, describes the *Phoenicians* as "rogues, bringing countless trinkets in their dark ships." These Semites early developed a most un-Semitic love of the sea, becoming the greatest seafaring race of antiquity. Not until the Venetian dogeships of the XI century A.D. would Mediterranean maritime trade again be so monopolized. From their city-states—Byblos, Tyre, Sidon, Ugarit, and Beirut—established two millennia before Christ, Phoenicians controlled commerce in the Mediterranean and even into the Atlantic by the beginning of the first millennium B.C. Carthage was founded by Phoenicians.

It was Phoenician workmen whom the Assyrian kings employed to make the furniture and metal work for the royal palaces. King Solomon (970 B.C.) likewise engaged them in building the Hebrew Temple. They were famous for the royal purple dyestuffs extracted from the gland of the murex, a sea snail. Yes, they traded for ivory, gold, tin, silver, and fine woods, and they shanghaied foreigners for their slave trade. Indeed, almost single-handed they furnished the harems of the contemporary world with the girls they abducted. They stole from the weak, swindled the gullible, and practiced piracy. Phoenicians were great imitators and transmitters of culture, but they were not great inventors. They marketed fine things, but the original idea, including the alphabet often ascribed to them, almost invariably sprang from elsewhere. The style of their merchandise was international.

Their cities and monuments are largely gone, but such few works of Phoenician art which have been found resemble those of Egypt or Babylonia (Nos. 5, 7, 8). However, they were truly bearers of civilization. Alexander the Great destroyed their eastern cities. Hannibal of Carthage was a son of this unique breed of merchant seafarers, and in the Punic Wars, a thousand years later, as we shall see in the following Section, Rome herself felt the mettle of the last outpost of the Phoenicians.

Now we consider the *Indo-European* dispersal, the sequence in all history most germane to western man, embracing his ancestry. Precisely as the southern grasslands on the margins of the deserts of Arabia originally furnished the reservoirs of unsettled Semites so, from the northern grasslands, stretching from the lower Danube eastward along the north shore of the Black Sea through southern Russia and far into Asia, the Indo-Europeans emerged from their biological matrix. Ethnologists originally believed that they originated in the Pamir highlands; later theories place them from Turkestan or Siberia. They are the most important branch of the Caucasian race. They bear the Indo-European name because their migrations led them, along diverging routes, to an extended, imposing line from the frontiers of India on the east, westward across all Europe to the Atlantic. This great northern line was confronted on the south by the line of the Semitic people. The history of the ancient Near Eastern world is that of the struggle of these two lines until the Indo-European triumph.

We are able to follow the Indo-Europeans from their dispersion, about 2300 B.C. Their numerous tribes roamed the steppes and the highlands seeking pasturage for their cattle and sheep. They cultivated grains, chiefly barley. They early knew copper, from which they made murderous axes which later served them well in the conquest of Europe. And their early monopoly of the horse gave them a tremendous superiority over all their adversaries. But they did not develop writing, and hence had little government. Through wanderings, the tribes lost contact with each other. Local peculiarities and customs became more marked until they lost all knowledge of their original kinship. But philology can trace their language across Europe into India, viz:

WEST				EAST	
English	German	Latin	Greek	Persian	Sanskrit
Brother	Bruder	Frāter	Phrātēr	Brātar	Bhratar
Mother	Mutter	Māter	Mētēr	Mātar	Mātar
Father	Vater	Pater	Patēr	Pitar	Pitar

Indo-European peregrinations—we have just left the vanguard Hittites and Mittani; the Achaeans settled in Greece, from whence they set out on the conquest of Crete and the Aegean; the Aryans made their way to the Indus; the Cimmerians (Nos. 15, 16) and, later the Scythians (No. 23), made their homes on the Russian steppes; the Thracians and the Phrygians occupied Asia Minor and Syria. Of similar origin were the Celts, the Slavs, and the Germans who later, strong in the possession of iron weapons, spread via the Danube route. Sprung from these roots, the Greek and Latin branches prospered, and later barbarian shoots grew ever stronger until at length they overshadowed the entire Occidental world. However, in this Section we confine ourselves to the Near East, so we will follow the Indo-European Medes and Persians to the expiry of the Semitic world.

Again history was meteoric. In a tiny, obscure *Elamite* kingdom around 550 B.C., a vassal of the Medes, Cyrus the Great, the Achaemenid, the extraordinary *Persian*, trained skillful archers whose hail of arrows at long range overwhelmed his enemies before they could engage in the previously customary hand-to-hand fighting. Then his superb horsemen completed their destruction. His genius conquered all of his neighbors, including the *Medes* (No. 21) and the *Lurs* (Nos. 14, 17)—a spectacle which filled the eyes of the west with wonder and alarm. The great states—Chaldean-Babylonia, Egypt, Lydia, and even Sparta in Greece—formed a coalition against him. Straightway Cyrus captured the Lydian capital, Sardis, and the fabled treasure of its King Croesus. Within five years the power of the little Persian kingdom had swept across Asia Minor, and it became the leading state in the western Orient. Turning east, he entered Babylon seemingly without resistance. Archaeology has dissipated historians' confusion about this episode with the discovery of a chronological tablet containing the annals of Nabonidos. It now appears that the Biblical reconstruction in the Book of Daniel is erroneous. However, the Semitic World ascendancy was dead, destroyed by Indo-Europeans. Cyrus' son Cambyses II conquered Egypt (becomes monotonous), and ultimately the Persian Empire extended from the Delta almost to India. Persia became the great empire of pre-Roman antiquity. We shall leave the Persian-Greek Wars to the next section, as they were infinitely more important to Greece than to Persia. Iran, now Persia's official name, was its ancient designation.

Several of the early Persian kings, in contrast to the Assyrians, appear to have been humane and tolerant for Oriental autocrats. The Empire adopted the religious teachings of Zoroaster who held that there was only one God. Six centuries before Christ, thus spoke Zarathustra. But the Persians were not ripe for monotheism and achieved a dualistic compromise with the Evil One as a positive force and satellite divinities. By the end of the V century B.C. internal decay appeared in the Persian State, and 331 B.C. marked the destruction of the Achaemenid Empire by Alexander the Great's Macedonians. After Alexander's death, most of Persia fell to the *Seleucids,* a dynasty founded by one of his generals. Though they introduced a fruitful Hellenistic culture, they were unable to maintain control. *Parthia* (No. 24), which broke away in the mid III century B.C., became a semi-successor to the old Persian Empire and later even came to rival Rome. Parthia's decline was followed by the establishment of the neo-Persian Empire in A.D. 226 under the *Sasanians.* This magnificent state endured until, in A.D. 650, invading Arabs replaced Zoroastrianism with Islam, and the caliphate made Persia part of a larger pattern from which modern Iran later emerged.

In Persian art, the *Zoroastrian* cult contributed the basis for symbolism. It is a rarity to receive remote history first hand, but we have eye witness accounts of the glories of Babylon written by Herodotus at about 450 B.C. According to him the city wall was fifty-three miles long with a road atop wide enough to accommodate a four-horse chariot. He even describes, in addition to bridges, a tunnel under the Euphrates. For a recital of Babylon's grandeurs, reread the Book of Esther. Persepolis (Takht-i-Jamshid), the ritual capital of Darius and Xerxes (No. 22), employs columns that are taller, more slender, and more closely fluted than those of Greece. Here were the fabulous addorsed bulls and lion at the Palace Gates. The sculpture is stylization subtly combined with realism. Outstanding among minor arts is exquisite metalwork. For five hundred years after Alexander's conquest, Persian art is strongly influenced by Hellenistic and Roman motifs (No. 25). Then under the Sasanians there was a revival of native aesthetic feeling. Sybaritically decorated palaces were built. Painting was encouraged. Carvings, especially in ivory, were extraordinary (No. 27). Finally the VII century saw the merging of Persian and Islamic cultures.

The *Byzantine Empire,* the core of which was in Asia Minor and extended through the Balkans, belongs here, as, although it perpetuated Greco-Roman civilization, its dominant influence was Oriental. It was the eastern successor state to the Roman Empire, named for its capital, ancient Byzantium, long Constantinople and now Istanbul. Although it became permanent in A.D. 395 and continued for over a thousand years, it required amazing powers of survival as it was continually beset by Goths, Huns, Avars, Persians, Bulgars, Slavs, Arabs, Normans, Seljuks, French, and Italians. It stemmed the flow of Moslem conquest westward until, in 1453, it finally fell to the Ottoman Turks (Nos. 35, 36). But it carried the light while Europe slumbered through the Dark Ages. Byzantine art is a blend of Hellenistic and Oriental traditions. It reached its first golden age around A.D. 330 and except for the interruption caused by iconoclasm, its style persisted until the fall of Constantinople. It emphasized decorativeness, neglecting plasticity in favor of flatline harmony. Sculpture was characterized by flat, even relief, with delicate, lacy designs (No. 28). Mosaics (No. 29) reached a zenith in Ravenna and the cathedrals of Istanbul. Icon production flourished (Nos. 32, 33).

However, simultaneously with the advent of the Dark Ages in Europe, a great new world force arose in the Near East—the *World of Islam.* Mohammed, born in the remote Arabian Desert city of Mecca, was the prophet of the latest of the three great monotheisms. He drew upon Judaism and Christianity for the sacred book, the Koran. Islamic datings start from his flight, the Hegira, corresponding to A.D. 622 in the Christian calendar. The spread of the Moslems was phenomenally rapid in the VII and VIII centuries, and they soon were dominant from Moorish (Moslem) Spain to India, across Asia to the South Pacific, prevailed in North Africa, and today are still gaining converts. The art which the nomadic Moslems brought to the lands of the Mediterannean around the VII century was primarily ornamental. Religion forbade the making of idols. Hence, local styles, mainly Christian, were used to display surface decoration largely based on the arabesque, intertwined bands, and calligraphy (Nos. 26, 30, 31). The same emphasis appears in the minor arts of metalworking, pottery making, and rug weaving (No. 34). Geometric representation discourages idolatry.

Space has not permitted us here to review all of the currents and migrations of the proto-historic period. Nor can be delineated here personal stories—magnificent, tragic, horrific, humorous, and heroic, which these humans lived, loved, laughed, and wept. Today as one travels through the arid desert country of Iraq, Iran, and the Levantine States, it is difficult to realize that here great cities once flourished, mighty kings reigned, and gods in their temples were worshipped by multitudes. Beneath this wasteland are buried the secrets of millions of people undisturbed for thousands of years. But the slumbering wreckage of buried, ancient civilizations symbolizes neither futility nor *sic transit gloria mundi*, but the indomitability of man. Archaeology has found increasing sophistication of vernacular culture unaffected by the substitution of one ruling caste for another. Seaton Lloyd calls it "the pomp and squalor of these Oriental Bronze Age Kingdoms," prior to the advent of enlightenment from Greece. Included is a Chronology of the still partially beclouded sequences of these civilizations.

NEAR EASTERN SYNOPTIC CHRONOLOGY

CULTURE	APPROXIMATE AREA	APPROXIMATE PERIOD	CONQUERORS
Byzantine	From E. Siberia to Asia Minor extending to the S. Balkan Peninsula	A.D. 395 (East Rome)-1453	Seljuks (X-XII cent.), Tartars, Osmanli Turks
Sasanian	Persia	A.D. 224-649/650	Resisted Rome and Byzantium, overthrown by Arabs
Parthian	S.E. of Caspian Sea to India	250 B.C.-A.D. 226	Sasanians
Seleucid	Babylonia to Indus River	312 B.C.-A.D. 164	Rome
Persian-Mede (Achaemenid)	Iran (Later Assyria, Babylonia, Egypt, Greece, etc.)	VII century-331 B.C.	Parthia-Seleucia
Lydian	West Asia Minor (Croesus' Sardis)	687-540 B.C.	Persia
Scythian	North of Black Sea to the Crimea	IX-III century B.C.	After defeats by Persia and Greece, Sarmations succeeded
Phoenician	Mediterranean (Tyre, Byblos to Carthage)	1250-III century B.C.	Persia, Greece (Hellenistic)
Hebrew	Palestine	2300-1025 B.C.-A.D. 70	Canaanites, Egypt, Babylon, Rome
Phrygian	Central Asia Minor	1200-700 B.C.	Lydia, Gaul, Pergamum
Hittite Neo-Hittite	Asia Minor and Syria (Hattusas)	1800-1200-800 B.C.	Phrygia, Thracia, Assyria (Lydia successor)
Assyrian	West Asia (Assur, Nineveh) (681 B.C. Egypt)	1900-1200-612 B.C.	Second Babylonia briefly, then Persia
Babylonian-Chaldean	Mesopotamia (Lagash, Akkad, Erech, Ur)	1. Chaldean (625-538 B.C.) 2. Kassite (1740-1150 B.C.) 3. 3000-1800 B.C.	1. Persia 2. Assyria 3. Elam, Hittite, Kassite
Egyptian	N.E. Africa—Sinai Peninsula	3400 B.C.—various	Hyksos, Nubia, Assyria, Persia, Greece, Rome, etc.
Elamic	North of Persian Gulf (Susa)	4500-645 B.C.	Assyria
Sumer-Akkadian	South Mesopotamia (Ur, Eridu, Kish, Lagash)	5000-2300 B.C.	Rise of Elam, Babylonia

Following are examples in stone and metal wherein survive the boasts of rulers, the decorations of palaces and temples, votive pieces to propitiate gods, and a few examples of the aesthetics these human beings lived with. These were the people who brought our western civilization to the threshold. After this we will cross into Greek enlightenment.

From the Palace of the Assyrian King Ashurnasirpal II at Nimrud, the ancient Calah, on the River Tigris in the Mesopotamian Valley, sculpture No. 1 represents a winged genius kneeling before the sacred "tree of life." With others it dressed an interior wall of the great hall of the Northwest Palace and is one of a series, most of which are now in the British Museum and the Louvre. This alabaster gypsum is a greyish sulphate of lime, soft, susceptible to polish, but fragile.

Paint was used on these reliefs, although sparingly. Traces of black have been found on the hair, beard, and pupil; white on the eyeball. The headdress was red and the sandals, red and black. The effect, nevertheless, was that of plastic paintings. The horned tiara indicates his divine nature, but his short skirt and two wings signify that he is a messenger of the gods.

INSCRIPTION TRANSLATION:* PALACE OF ASHURNASIRPAL, GREAT KING, POWERFUL KING, KING OF THE LEGIONS, KING OF ASSYRIA; SON OF TUKULTI-URTA, GREAT KING, POWERFUL KING, KING OF THE LEGIONS, KING OF ASSYRIA—SON OF ADAD-NIRARI, GREAT KING, POWERFUL KING, KING OF THE LEGIONS, KING OF ASSYRIA; THE VALIANT WARRIOR WHO, WITH THE FAVOR OF THE GOD ASHUR, GOES AMONGST THE KINGS OF THE FOUR REGIONS, HAS NO RIVAL; A KING WHO SINCE THE CROSSING OF THE TIGRIS UNTO MOUNT LEBANON AND THE SEA, THE COUNTRY OF LAKÊ, IN ALL ITS EXTENT, THE COUNTRY OF SUHI, TO THE CITY OF RAPIKU, AT HIS FEET HAS SUBJUGATED THEM; FROM THE SOURCE OF SUBNAT TO NIRIB HIS HAND CONQUERED; FROM THE PASS OF KIKRURI TO THE LAND OF GILZANI, FROM THE FORD OF THE LOWER ZAB TO THE CITY OF TIL-BARI, WHICH IS ABOVE THE LANDS OF ZABAN; FROM TIL-SHA-ABTANI, AND TIL-SHA-ZABDANI, HIRIMU, HARATU, THE FORTRESSES OF KARDUNIASH (BABYLONIA); I ANNEXED TO WITHIN THE CONFINES OF MY COUNTRY; THE VAST COUNTRIES OF NAIRÎ; IN THEIR TOTALITY I SUBJUGATED; I BUILT ANEW THE CITY OF CALAH; I BUILT A PALACE OF MY SOVEREIGNTY FOR MY LORDLY PLEASURE FOR ALL TIME—I BUILT, ORNAMENTED, MADE MAGNIFICENT; BEASTS SUCH AS ONE SEES IN THE SEA AND ON THE MOUNTAINS, IN STONE I HAD FASHIONED AND IN FRONT OF THE PORTALS I MOUNTED THEM; AND SILVER, GOLD, LEAD, COPPER, AND IRON THE SPOIL OF THE LANDS WHICH I HAD BROUGHT UNDER MY SWAY, IN GREAT QUANTITIES I TOOK AND PLACED THEREIN.

*by Prof. P. Scheil, Académie Français

1. ASSYRIAN BAS RELIEF—GYPSEOUS ALABASTER— CA. 883-859 B.C.—H. 124 cm. (48½″)

This bas relief was excavated by Sir Austen Henry Layard in 1845. The top and bottom sections were separate when found. The top section, originally a much thicker slab of stone, was cleaned and thinned by the antiquary Fenardent, in Paris, December, 1911. A remarkably similar section is in the collection of the Archaeological Museum, Istanbul. H. Seyrig, then Director of the Louvre, certified this piece and granted us permission to bring it to this country. We also hold a letter dated January 26, 1961, from R. D. Barnett, Curator of Western Asiatic Antiquities at the British Museum, London, categorically authenticating it.

2. ASSYRIAN MEDALLION—GOLD—VII CENTURY B.C.— D. 7.1 cm. (2¾″)

A representational depiction of the Gilgamesh legend with the addorsed lions. (Refer to No. 14.) Found at Kaplantu in N.W. Iran, several elements of this purure survive, including similar examples in The Metropolitan Museum of Art, New York, and the Iran Bastan Museum, Tehran.

2a. ASSYRIAN TABLET—GYPSEOUS ALABASTER—CA. 883-859 B.C.—H. 42.5 cm. (16¾″)

2b. ASSYRIAN TABLET—GYPSEOUS ALABASTER—CA. 883-859 B.C.—H. 42.5 cm. (16¾″)

Here are two of the "Standard Tablets" in Nuzi Akkadian cuneiform, from the Palace of Ashurnasirpal II at Nimrud. In the translation opposite, it is interesting to note names, then contemporary, which appear in the Old Testament.

The Assyrian kings announced themselves in the land by means of the epithets they showered upon themselves in their inscriptions. But in the eyes of the harassed people they probably achieved partial godhead as the agent of divine retribution and the instrument of Jehovah's wrath. They were probably accepted on their own terms; hence, this is an early example of still prevalent demogogy.

[2a]

1. the beloved of Anu and Dagan, the str(ong one) . . .
2. Tukulti-Nin)-ib, the great king the mighty king, the king of
3. totality, king of Assyria; the son of Adad-nirari the (great) king goes hither and yon, and among the princes of the four quarters his rival (has not) . . .
4. the battle, the mighty flood who has no opponent . . .
5. brought the subjection, the mighty hero who has trampled on the neck of his foes . . .
6. of the strong, the king who with help of the great gods his lords
7. all of them he conquered, their tribute he received, taking
8. When Ashur, the lord who called me by my name, who made great . . .
9. my lordship entrusted, the wide (spread) troops of Lullumê . . .
10. With the help of Shamash and Adad, the gods my helpers . . .
11. (the country) Nirib, like Adad the destroyer I thundered . . .
12. (Leb)anon and the great sea, the land of Lakê in its whole extent
13. From the source of the river Subnat even to . . .
14. (from) . . . Kirruri even the land of Gilzani, from beyond . . .
15. above the land of Zaban, from the city of Til-sha-Zabdani . . .
16. (Kharu)tu, the fortress of Karduniash (i.e. Babylon) to the
17. as far as the land of Hashmar, I reckoned as the peoples of my land
18. my (governors I appointed, vassalage and service . . .

[2b]

1. (Nin)-ib, the beloved of Anu
2. (king) mighty, the king of totality, king of Assyria, the son of Tukulti Ninib
3. Assyria; the valiant hero, who with the help of Ashur
4. a rival has not, the wonderful shepherd
5. (oppon)ent does not have, the king who has brought to subjection those that were not subject to him
6. (who has tr)ampled on the neck of his foes and has trodden down
7. the king who with the help of the great gods his lords
8. (the high) lands all of them he conquered, their tribute
9. over all the lands. When Ashur, the Lord
10. his merciless weapon unto the power
11. Lul)lume, the widespread, in the midst of battle
12. (Sha)mash and Adad, the gods my helpers, the troops
13. (Niri)b, like Adad the destroyer I thundered.
14. Lebanon and the great sea
15. the city Rapiqi the cast into subjection under his feet
16. Urartu (i.e. Armenia) he conquered with his hand; from the pass
17. (lo)wer (Zab) even unto the city of Til-bari which is above the land of Zaban, from the city Til- . . .
18. the fortresses of Karduniash (i.e. Babylonia) I added to the borders of my land.

Lost beginning of the inscription: "The palace of Ashur-nasir-pal, the darling of Bel and Ninib, the beloved of Anu and Dagan" . . .

Translation by D. D. Luckenbill, *Ancient Records of Assyria and Babylonia*, Univ. of Chicago Press, 1926, Vol. I.

1

2

2a

2b

3. SUMERIAN BULL—STONE, GOLD, LAPIS LAZULI—EARLY III MILLENNIUM B.C.—L. 10.7 cm. (4³/₁₆″)

This masterful sculpture in creamy hardstone was found at ancient Ur, identified in the Bible as the home of Terah and of Abraham, on the lower Euphrates River in the Mesopotamian Valley. It is an extremely rare work. The indentations for the horns, ears, and eyes showed vestiges of the original gold, lapis, and nacreous material with which it had been decorated. The work has been restored in much the same manner a similar work in the collection of the University Museum, Philadelphia, was treated.

4. SUMERIAN WORSHIPPER FIGURE—ALABASTER—FIRST HALF III MILLENNIUM B.C.—H. 30.1 cm. (11½″)

The site of today's Tell Hariri on the middle Euphrates River is the antique locus of that powerful city-state Mari, one of the earliest centers of civilization over six thousand years ago. The excavations at Mari begun by A. Parrot in 1933 still continue. A great capital has emerged from these ruins. Monuments, sculpture, wall-paintings, and artifacts attest that Mari was an outstanding art center. Here 25,000 clay tablets with cuneiform script—a complete library constituting the diplomatic and economic archives of the State—tell the story not only of this city-state but also of all Mesopotamia. These Sumerians worshipped idols, but they also deposited likenesses of themselves in their temples, seemingly to continue worship in their absence. Here is one of the figurines, in an attitude of supplication, with hands clasped in fervent prayer and with huge, vacant eyes gazing heavenward as though in an hypnotic trance. These strange eyes originally had corneas of bone and eyelids of bitumen. All of these figurines wear the garments known as *kaunakes*, made of strips of cloth which are a conventionalized representation of sheep's fleece. The recurrent geometric lines, protruding shoulders, angular elbows, and trapezoidal trunk obviously evolved with a view to their power of suggestion. The absence of a beard shows the figure to be of the first dynasties—Pre-Sargonid Pe-

riod. This is further borne out by the unmistakable fidelity of the Semitic type of individuality. Ex. Coll. K. Rabenou, New York.

4a. SUMERIAN TABLETS—CLAY—EARLY II MILLENNIUM B.C.—H. 25 mm.-30 mm. (1″-1¼″)

Mari, destroyed by Hammurabi in the XVIII century B.C., has yielded thousands of clay tablets inscribed in cuneiform. These documents reflect legal, political, religious, and business affairs that took place nearly 4,000 years ago.

5. PROTO-PHOENICIAN AX—BRONZE—1900-1600 B.C.— L. 11.7 cm. (4⅝″)

It is proper to apply the term Phoenician only after the XII century B.C. when the Canaanites were assimilated by the invading Aegeans or Sea People to form a new race. Previously they were not referred to as an ethnic group, but by the names of their cities—Ugarit, Arvad, Simyra, Berutians, Sidonians, or Tyrians. During the Middle Bronze Age their battle axes were fashioned in this unique shape. Found at Byblos.

6. CANAANITE FIGURE—BRONZE—LATE II MILLENNIUM B.C.—H. 12 cm. (4¾″)

This piece, excavated below No. 7 at the same site, poses a problem of attribution, possibly Aramaean.

7. PHOENICIAN FIGURE—BRONZE—EARLY I MILLENNIUM B.C.—H. 9.6 cm. (3¾″)

This figure, found at Sidon, shows great vitality in its modeling. Unusual condition.

8. PHOENICIAN FIGURE—SILVER—EARLY I MILLENNIUM B.C.—H. 6.4 cm. (2½″)

From Byblos, this figure in silver shows the Phoenican style. Gift of that eminent Beirut scholar Fouad Alouf.

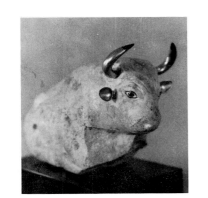

3

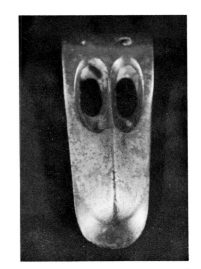

4a

5

6

4

7

8

8a. BABYLONIAN SEAL (FIRST DYNASTY)—CRYSTAL—
2225-1875 B.C.—25 mm. x 12 mm. (1″ x ⁷/₁₆″)

8b. CHALDEAN SEAL—CARNELIAN—VII CENTURY B.C.—
30 mm. x 15 mm. (1¼″ x ⅝″)

8c. SUMER-AKKADIAN SEAL—BLACK MARBLE—
3000-2700 B.C.—36 mm. x 20 mm. (1⅜″ x ¾″)

Cylinder seals were used as a means of identifying ownership
or authentication, and by extension their impressions were worn
as amulets. Inasmuch as all ancients of any importance possessed their seal, many examples from many early civilizations
have come down to us. They evolved into miniature sculptures
of great quality. They often depicted court scenes and votive
rites.

9. ELAMITE FIGURINE—BLACK STEATITE—CA. 2000 B.C.—
H. 6.2 cm. (2½″)

Few examples of Elamite sculpture are extant. This bears a great
resemblance to earlier Sumerian style. The *Encyclopedie Photographique de l'Art* (Louvre) shows a similar figure. An inscription on the back makes identification possible. Said to have
been found at Susa. Ex. Coll. Joseph Brummer, Paris.

10. BABYLONIAN ISHTAR—TERRA COTTA—FIRST HALF
II MILLENNIUM B.C.—H. 13.7 cm. (5⅜″)

Ishtar, chief goddess of Babylonia-Assyria, was the Semitic deity
identified with the Sumerian virgin mother goddess, which
evolved to Rome's Venus. Sacred prostitution formed a part of
her cult. She is shown here as a human figure with a bird-like
head, typically Babylonian, although figures of this type appear
as far west as Syria and Lebanon. A similar figure is in The
Metropolitan Museum.

11. BABYLONIAN FIGURE—BRONZE—CA. 1500 B.C.—H. 11.5
cm. (4½″)

From the Second Babylonian Period, this bearded warrior carries a spear and dagger. Mint condition.

12. PRE-HITTITE FIGURE—BRONZE—EARLY II MILLEN-
NIUM B.C.—H. 10.6 cm. (4⅛″)

We found small votive bronzes at Alacahoyuk. Very possibly
this represents the god Hadad as he appears to be wearing the
Egyptian crown surmounted by the disc to which are added the
horns of the Babylonian genii. If so, this would indeed be an
early connection between Cappadocia and Egypt.

13. HITTITE FIGURE—BRONZE—CA. 1200 B.C.—
H. 11.7 cm. (4⅝″)

Both arms of this figurine are lifted as though in supplication.
From the Bogazkoy area where many inscriptions in Hittite or
Kanesian, Babylonian, Luish, and Khattish have been uncovered.

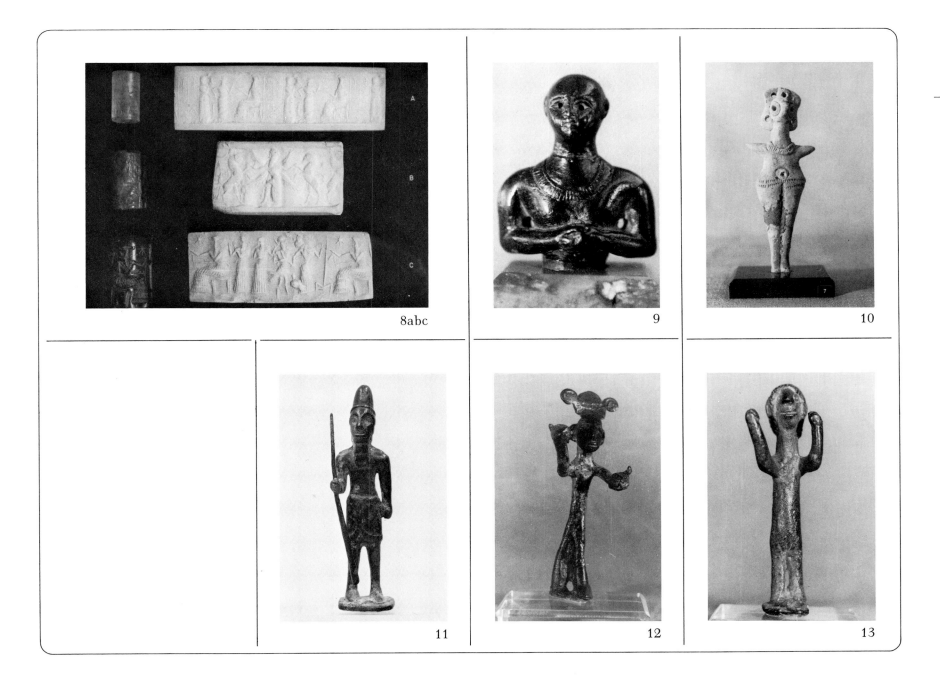

8abc

9

10

11

12

13

14. LURISTAN FINIAL—BRONZE—VIII-VII CENTURY B.C.—
H. 19.4 cm. (7⅝″)

Such bronzes, found in many Lur tombs in western Iran, are composed of a bottle-shaped base, an idol, and a long spike with a carved head. The idol proper was fastened to the base by the spike. This idol interprets in a highly stylized, almost distorted fashion, the theme of the hero Gilgamesh wrestling with the addorsed wild beasts. Arthur Upham Pope found stylistic similarities between Luristan bronzes and those of early dynastic China.

15. MANNAEAN(?) IBEX HEAD—GOLD—LATE IX-
EARLY VII CENTURY B.C.—L. 6.9 cm. (2¾″)

In 1947 a buried treasure hoard of gold, silver, and ivory was found in the northwestern Iranian province of Kurdistan at Ziwiye by peasants. A few other pieces, including this zoomorphic handle, were found at nearby Ghaflantou. All were rapidly dispersed and passed into the hands of private collectors. André Parrot states in his fine book, *The Arts of Assyria*, that the most characteristic pieces of the Ziwiye treasure have now all been traced and classified. This treasure has been widely published both in technical publications and in the lay press and magazines. Attribution is uncertain. The motif of our ibex belongs in the Assyrian repertory, but its suavity is reminiscent of the gold work found in not too distant Scythian graves—"the art of the steppes." At any rate, the technique is superb. The specialist Godard regards these pieces as products of a local Mannaean school. These Mannaeans, the Old Testament Manni, were an autochthonous people whose kingdom flourished in this area at this time and seems to have acted as a buffer state between the Urartians and the Assyrians until conquered by Media. Exhibited: "7000 Ans d'Art en Iran," Paris, 1961.

16. AMLASH ZEBU—BURNISHED RED TERRA COTTA—
X-VIII CENTURY B.C.—L. 35.1 cm. (13⅞″)

Recent excavations near the small village of Amlash, in Iran's Dailaman region, just south of the Caspian Sea, have produced a variety of extraordinary examples of the potter's skill. Many appear to be cult figures. Here is one of the striking bulls found in the area.

17. LURISTAN FINIAL—BRONZE—VIII-VII CENTURY B.C.—
H. 11.2 cm. (4⅜″)

From the Kermanshah district of Iran, this square open work spike head shows a goddess with two lions. Fine green patina. Cf. *Encyclopedie Photographique de l'Art*, Vol. II, pl. 35/A (Louvre).

18. SYRIAC ASTARTE—TERRA COTTA—CA. 1000 B.C.—
H. 10.2 cm. (4″)

The nature goddess Astarte possessed the attitudes of fertility and reproduction. As the patroness of the hunt, she was identified with Artemis. Hence, following her prototype, Ishtar (No. 10) there was a consequent fusion in myth and legend. Found in Syria near Tyre, this idol is probably of Phoenician origin.

19. SYRIAC HORSEMAN—BRONZE—CA. VII CENTURY B.C.—
H. 9.1 cm. (3⅝″)

A relic of this area's heterogeneous nomadic peoples, this mounted figure was found near Ras Shamra, Syria, formerly Ugarit. Ex. Coll. G. Zacos, Istanbul.

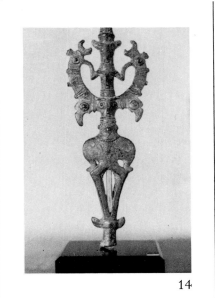

14

17

16

15

18

19

20. ASSYRIAN RELIEF—CALCAREOUS STONE—
709-705 B.C.—H. 26.4 cm. (10⅜″)

This face portrays the same features as the Sargon II large reliefs found by Botta, now in the Louvre. It is from Khorsabad. Vestiges of color remain. This is the Sargon sometimes called Sharrukin, who completed Shalmaneser's conquest of Samaria, taking Carchemish, destroying the northern Israelite Kingdom and subduing Babylon. He appropriated the name of the original, legendary Sargon of Akkad whose vast Mesopotamian Empire existed two millennia before him.

21. MEDIAN SEAL—GREEN STONE—VII CENTURY B.C.—
D. 6.1 cm. (2⅜″)

The Medes were of the early Indo-European peoples who supplanted the Semites and briefly ruled over Persia. They had been the first subjects of tyrannical Assyria to secure their freedom. But Cyrus the Great soon incorporated them into his Persian Achaemenid Empire. Since there are no Median records, the Bible, Assyrian, and Greek sources must be relied upon for Median history. Therein the Persians are called Parsuans and the Medes, Madai. Few artifacts can be ascribed to the Medes. This extraordinarily large intaglio carving depicting two stylized animals was found at Poshte Kouh, Iran. It has obviously been worn. Ex. Coll. K. Rabenou, New York.

22. ACHAEMENID PERIOD RELIEF—HARD SLATE—500-485 B.C.—W. 19.3 cm. (7⅝″)

This relief, the head of a royal Persian guard, is a fragment from the staircase of Persepolis, the ancient ceremonial capital of the Persian Empire under Darius and Xerxes. The vast and wondrous ritual city was destroyed by fire by Alexander the Great. Achaemenid Period. The sculpture is particularly sharp. Cf. Eric Schmidt, *Persepolis*, (Chicago, 1954), Vol. II, pl. 50.

23. SCYTHIAN PLAQUE—BRONZE—IV CENTURY B.C.—
W. 10.8 cm. (4¼″)

China, Mesopotamia, and Greece—the peoples of these ancient lands knew and feared the Scythians. These Eurasians, speaking an Indo-European tougue, were early mounted warriors. Their "animal style" art, which excited Peter the Great of Russia, formed the basis for European heraldry and much of ecclesiastical symbolism. Their saga and their customs warrant a reading of Rice's *The Scythians* referred to in the bibliography. We have seen much beautiful Scythian toreutic art in gold and bronze in Russia, but there is little outside due to restrictions. This pastoral scene, executed in bronze, comes from Cimmeria, modern Kuban, on the Black Sea. Exhibited: Iranian Institute, "Persian Art," New York, 1940. Ex. Coll. Christian R. Holmes.

24. PARTHIAN FLASK HANDLE—BRONZE—II CENTURY
—H. 23.2 cm. (9⅛″)

The Parthians, of Scythian origin, were famous horsemen and archers, generally mercenaries, serving the Assyrian and Persian Empires. They established a great empire themselves around 250 B.C., which lasted for over 500 years. The modern plastic flask approximates the shape of the original and serves as a mount for the bronze. The expression "a Parthian shot" came from the Parthian ruse of pretending to flee in order to shoot their arrows at their pursuers more successfully.

20

21

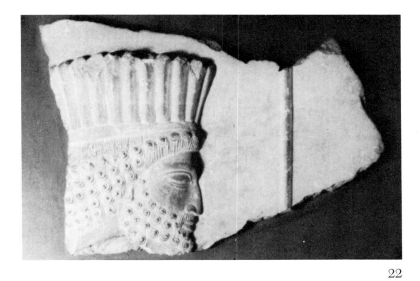

22

23

24

25. SYRIAC STELE—LIMESTONE—III CENTURY—
H. 53 cm. (20⅞″)

This sepulchral stele is from the magnificent ruins of Palmyra
in the Syrian desert, once one of the most important caravan-
serai cities. It sealed the tomb of a mother and child. The inscription shows traces of color. Rostovtzeff says, "The sculpture of
Palmyra is the Hellenized offspring of Aramaean and Anatolian
plastic art." Ex. Coll. Azeez Khayat, Haifa.

26. PERSIAN FRAGMENT—SANDSTONE—MID XIII
CENTURY—H. 61.1 cm. (24″)

A similar stone relief, probably the end piece of a balustrade, is
illustrated in Dimand's *Handbook of Muhammadan Art*, inscribed with the name of the sculptor, the owner, and the date.
A rich, almost baroque style in Persia under the Mongols
evolved, which this example illustrates. Found at Hamadan,
Iran.

27. PERSIAN PLAQUE—IVORY—V CENTURY—
L. 10.4 cm. (4⅛″)

Under the Sasanian Dynasty, Hellenistic and Roman motifs disappeared in Persia, and there was a resurgence of native aesthetics. The architecture became sybaritic, but excellent paintings,
repoussé work in precious metals, and ivory carvings were created. This ivory example with characteristic Sasanian scrolling,
foliate branches is one of few examples that have come down to
us. Found at Mazanderan, Iran.

28. BYZANTINE CAPITAL—MARBLE—VII CENTURY—
W. 40.1 cm. (15¾″)

This capital in the full round was found near Homs, Syria, and
topped a column at the ruins of a Byzantine palace. Through
Homs passed the traffic of Egypt, Palestine, and Damascus to
the northern lands and its plain was the battleground of warring
nations. Here is an example of Byzantine sculpture showing the
principle of construction in light, wherein the artist painted
with his chisel. The preoccupation is not the pattern in terms of
light but the color effect produced by the shadow variations
which are determined by the shallowness and depth of cutting.

29. BYZANTINE MOSAIC—MARBLE AND PLASTER—
V CENTURY—W. 68.2 cm. (26⅞″)

This panel is from the border of a pavement from a private villa
in Daphne Harbie, a residential suburb of ancient Antioch,
founded in 300 B.C. by Seleucus and once one of the world's largest trade centers. Here followers of Jesus were first called Christians. This piece is fret ornamented with guilloche and ribbon
motif. It was excavated by the Antioch Project of the Baltimore
Museum of Art, from which it was purchased.

30. PERSIAN MINIATURE—INK AND POLYCHROME ON
PAPER—XVI CENTURY—H. 20.3 cm. (8″)

The unique art of miniature painting was principally fostered
by the court. These manuscripts were not hung but served as
elaborate book illustrations. This painting of a Safavid monarch
seated under a canopy surrounded by courtiers and servants is
from Shiraz. Intricate calligraphy, esteemed more than painting, is visible through the reverse side of the frame.

25

26

27

28

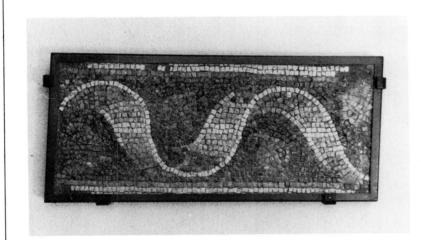

29

30

31. PERSIAN INTAGLIO—MARBLE—XII CENTURY—
H. 47.8 cm. (18¾″)

Known as a *mihrab*, this Moslem prayer niche served as a tomb-stone for some Persian lady during the Seljuk Dynasty. The Kufic inscription praising the deceased and quoting from the Koran bears a date corresponding to A.D. 1132. This is from Nishapur in Khorasan, reputed birthplace of Omar Khayyam.

32. BYZANTINE TRIPTYCH—WOOD, GOLD LEAF, AND
PAINT—XVI CENTURY—W. 38.3 cm. (15⅛″)

Ikons were venerated in the Eastern Orthodox Church. These examples are actually post-Byzantine but are so called. This triptych is in a fine, unrestored condition. We obtained it in Yugoslavia, through the kind intercession of Professor Lavarevic of the Zagreb Ethnographical Museum.

33. BYZANTINE IKON—WOOD, GOLD LEAF, AND PAINT—
XVII CENTURY—H. 30.2 cm. (11⅞″)

This ikon is from the Dodecanese Islands in the East Aegean Sea. It shows strong Oriental influence. The meticulous brush work in this and No. 32 above can be best appreciated under a glass. Ex. Coll. Meptinoz, Athens.

34. TWO RHODIAN TILES—ENAMELED POTTERY—
XVI CENTURY—L. 48.1 cm. (19″)

The use of lustered tiles for the decoration of dwellings, public buildings, mosques, and tombs was prevalent in the Islamic World. These examples are from the kilns of Isnik, once the most important ceramic center in Asia Minor. The decoration consists of Iranian palmettes and floral motifs also characteristic of Turkish art. These potters were masters of under-glaze decoration painted in cobalt blue, turquoise blue, green, yellow, and a superb tomato red. A large panel of exactly these same tiles is in The Metropolitan Museum, New York, and is reproduced in color in Dimand's *Handbook of Muhammadan Art*, 1944.

35. PERSIAN LION—BRONZE—XI-XII CENTURY—
H. 15.4 cm. (6⅛″)

Seljuk was the name of the ruling family of Ghuzz Turkoman tribes which invaded western Asia during the XI century, founding dynasties in Persia, Syria, and Asia Minor. They formed the beginning of the Turkish Empire in western Asia. These bronzes were the stands of incense burners. Crusty patina.

36. PERSIAN LION—BRONZE—XI-XII CENTURY—
H. 16.2 cm. (6⅜″)

For description refer to No. 35 above. This lion is infinitely more sophisticated than his companion piece. A white inlay still marks the eyes and probably originally filled the other incisions.

31

32

33

34

35

36

37. EGYPTIAN SCRIBE—DIORITE—V DYNASTY—CA. 2470-2320 B.C.—H. 35.1 cm. (13⅞″)

This is a representation of a scribe measuring grain. It was found in a mastaba at Sakkara. The man is not wearing a wig. A contrast exists between the bulk of the rather heavy body and the finesse of the attentive expression of the face. It dates from the close of the Ancient Kingdom, and it is remarkable that a sculptor of that period could achieve such a skillful work without a trace of archaism. Registered number 344 in the Control Book for the Service of Egyptian Antiquities, September 16, 1944.

38. EGYPTIAN STELE—LIMESTONE—XXX DYNASTY—CA. 380-343 B.C.—H. 64.3 cm. (25¼″)

From the Valley of the Kings, this stele bears two cartouches and the portrait of the last pharaoh, Nectanebes II, wearing the crowns of the Upper and Lower Nile. Ex. Coll. Albert Eid, Cairo.

39. EGYPTIAN STELE—LIMESTONE, STUCCO—XXVI DYNASTY—CA. 663-525 B.C.—H. 62.9 cm. (24¾″)

This is the stele of Amon-Mose, possibly from Sais. Authenticated by William Christopher Hayes, former Curator of Egyptian Art, The Metropolitan Museum, New York.

40. EGYPTIAN STELE—LIMESTONE—V DYNASTY—CA. 2470-2320 B.C.—W. 32.2 cm. (12¾″)

Relatively few examples of Egyptian painting have escaped the ravages of time and man. However, all of the Pharaomic reliefs and steles were once vivaciously colored, although not a trace remains on most of them today. The effect must have been, by modern standards, unbearably garish. More or less vivid red ochre was used on male figures while yellow, pink, or pale brown were reserved for women. All pigments consisted of natural substances ground to a powder. These have oxidized and darkened over the centuries. Many murals, though, especially those of Thebes, are in a marvelous state of preservation. As in Greece, painting and sculpture went hand in hand. Should we regard colored reliefs as sculpture painted over, or as painting on a surface chiseled or modeled? This man with his hand upon the neck of a gazelle was found in an Old Kingdom tomb.

41. EGYPTIAN STELE—LIMESTONE—XII-XIII DYNASTY—CA. 1750 B.C.—H. 79.1 cm. (31⅛″)

Here is an example of a family stele, tracing genealogy. It was found at Beni Hasan. Authenticated by William Christopher Hayes, former Curator of Egyptian Art, The Metropolitan Museum, New York.

37

38

39

40

41

42. EGYPTIAN RAM—GRANITE—XXX DYNASTY—
CA. 380-343 B.C.—H. 21.4 cm. (8½″)

The Ram, Khnoum, was worshipped at Philae, now submerged by the dam, where this was found. Frequently represented as a ram-headed man, it is a symbol of Amon in his procreative capacity.

43. EGYPTIAN RELIEF—LIMESTONE—XVIII DYNASTY—
1557-1304 B.C.—H. 25.2 cm. (9⅞″)

Some color remains upon this relief of a woman holding a lotus flower. Provenance unknown.

44. EGYPTIAN HEAD—BLACK BASALT—XXIV DYNASTY—
CA. 730-712 B.C.—H. 16.5 cm. (6½″)

This head of a woman has been described by Jacques Vandier of the Louvre as "an admirable portrait made by a master sculptor." The convolutions of the hair must have posed a technical problem over 2500 years ago.

45. EGYPTIAN OSTRACA—BAKED TILE—XIX DYNASTY—
CA. 1304-1200 B.C.—H. 12.1 cm. (4¾″)

Ostracas were allegedly used as a preliminary sketch by the artist before embarking on a full-scale picture. This was found at the Theban Necropolis.

46. EGYPTIAN FRAGMENT—LIMESTONE—XXVI DYNASTY
—663-525 B.C.—H. 28.6 cm. (11¼″)

The hand upon the top of this fragment suggests that it was once part of a large statue. It is engraved with divinities and hieroglyphic inscriptions. Saite Period.

47. EGYPTIAN OSTRACA—CARVED LIMESTONE— XIX-XX
DYNASTY—CA. 1304-1185 B.C.—H. 11.8 cm. (4⅝″)

This is a lovely, sharp carving. It was found at the Theban Necropolis.

42

43

44

45

46

47

48. EGYPTIAN FIGURE—GRANITE—XIII DYNASTY—
CA. 1785-1660 B.C.—H. 24.2 cm. (9½″)

This portrait-statuette of Mer-Sekhem-Ra has an inscription upon the reverse side. Registered number 343 in the Control Book for the Service of Egyptian Antiquities, Cairo, September 16, 1944.

49. EGYPTIAN SHAWABTY—DECORATED FAIENCE—XXI DYNASTY—CA. 1185-950 B.C.—H. 17.3 cm. (6⅞″)

These mummiform funerary figures were deposited in the tombs of the dead and were to serve as substitutes in the work gangs of the hereafter. Hence at times dozens of them were found in a single burial. Of brilliant turquoise blue, this bears the name of Nesi-Khonso, wife of Psusennes II, priestess of Amon.

50. EGYPTIAN FALCON—BRONZE—XXVI DYNASTY—
663-525 B.C.—H. 27.1 cm. (10⅝″)

The falcon, Horus, was the chief god of Upper Egypt. After the Nile Delta had been conquered by Upper Egypt, the Pharaohs used Horus as a prefix to their name, being the incarnation of the principal god. It was also the symbolic representation of the Sun. Saite Period. Fine detail.

51. EGYPTIAN LUG JAR—DIORITE—PRE-DYNASTIC—
BEFORE 3000 B.C.—H. 13.1 cm. (5⅛″)

This jar was found by Professor Garstaing of Liverpool University. Ex. Coll. G. H. Rea, Liverpool.

52. EGYPTIAN FISH—BRONZE—XXVI-XXX DYNASTY—
663-343 B.C.—L. 12.4 cm. (4⅞″)

The snouted Nile perch was commonly placed in burials as provision for the life beyond. This statuette carries cow's horns and the sun disk and is mounted on a shallow plinth.

53. EGYPTIAN BOWL—ALABASTER—XVIII DYNASTY—
CA. 1557-1304 B.C.—W. 13.4 cm. (5¼″)

This translucent alabaster bowl is Ex. Coll. Albert Eid, Cairo.

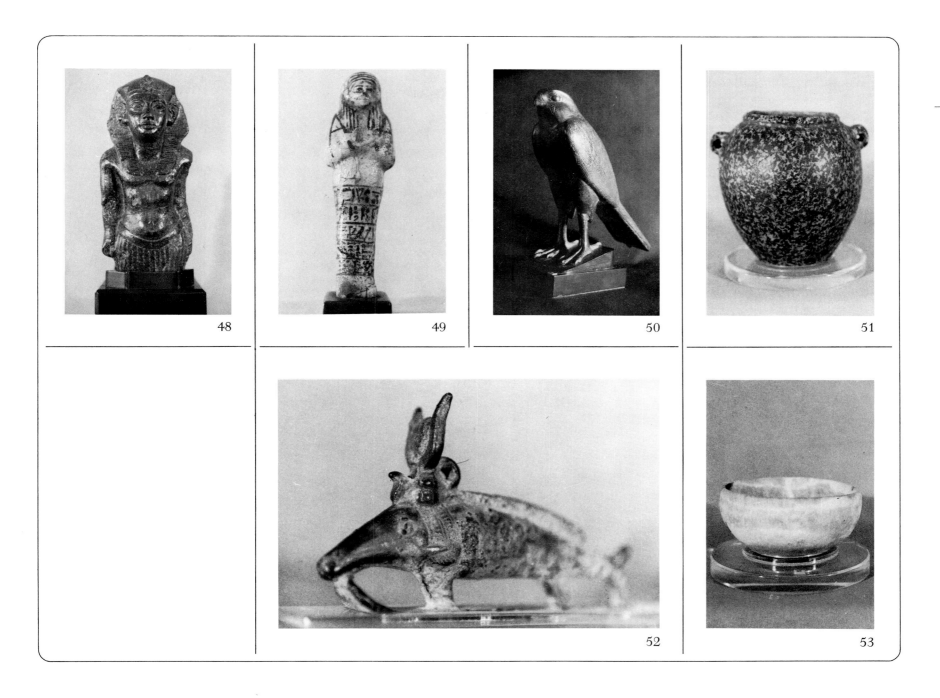

48

49

50

51

52

53

54. EGYPTIAN FIGURE—BRONZE—XXIX DYNASTY—
CA. 380 B.C.—H. 31.5 cm. (12⅜″)

The bronze of the Pharaoh Psmouthis has his name and pro-name inscribed in hieroglyphs at his feet upon the base. The object in his hands has religious significance as his coffin. His eyes appear to be small inset rubies. The work is dated. Registered number 936 in the Control Book for the Service of Egyptian Antiquities, Cairo, September 26, 1946.

55. EGYPTIAN HEADPIECE—BRONZE—PTOLEMAIC PERIOD
—CA. 304-30 B.C.—H. 10.4 cm. (4¼″)

This headpiece has a recess for a plume or other ornament. The hinge is most interesting as it enables the wearer to fit it to the head. The design, including Isis and scarabs, is finely engraved. Much of the original patination was removed in cleaning. Ex. Coll. Albert Eid, Cairo.

56. COPTIC GABLE—LIMESTONE—V CENTURY—
W. 88 cm. (34⅝″)

By ancient tradition, the Apostle Mark arrived in Alexandria about A.D. 50 carrying the Gospel to the Egyptians. The opulence and intellectual feats of that fabled city were fading under the rising glory of Rome. Masterpieces of Greco-Egyptian civilization still existed, but there began the last great cultural period of ancient Egypt, the Christian culture known as the Coptic Period. By A.D. 50 Christians outnumbered pagans. The development of the Christian Coptic sect is of artistic and historical importance. The Copts decorated their churches and monasteries with carved limestone and beautiful fabrics, employing a combination of Hellenistic, Oriental, and Christian motifs. These greatly influenced the medieval art of Spain and southern France and may be regarded as a source and inspiration of Romanesque art. This gable is from the monastery of Sohag near Akhmim in Upper Egypt. Exhibited: Brooklyn Museum, "Pagan and Christian Egypt," 1941, illus. 57. Published: D. G. Kelekian. *Important Documents of Coptic Art.* New York: Harbor Press, n.d.

57. SYRO-COPTIC LION—LIMESTONE—VI CENTURY—
H. 26.3 cm. (10⅜″)

The Copts penetrated the eastern littoral. A similar work is in the Damascus Museum, Syria.

59. GRECO-EGYPTIAN ENCAUSTIC—WAX AND WOOD—
II-III CENTURY—H. 32.6 cm. (12⅞″)

This is the mummy portrait of a bearded young man and comes from the Fayum. Encaustic painting earlier was done by the ancient Greeks by heating or burning pigment in wax, rendering the colors permanent.

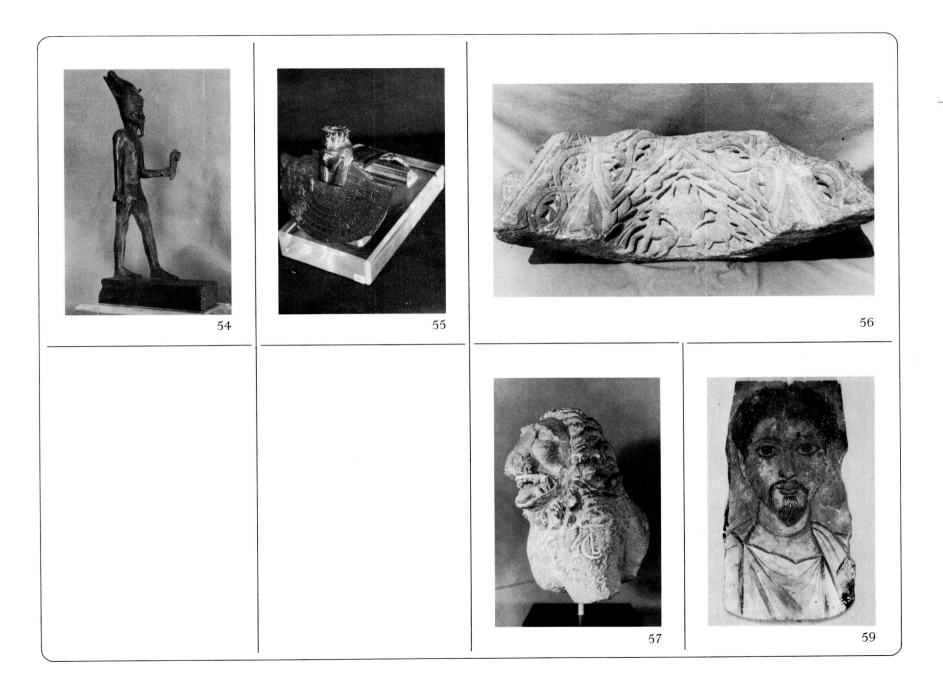

54

55

56

57

59

DETAIL OF GALLO-ROMAN MOSAIC PAVEMENT (CATALOG NO. 101)

SECTION II. GREECE, ROME, AND THE WEST

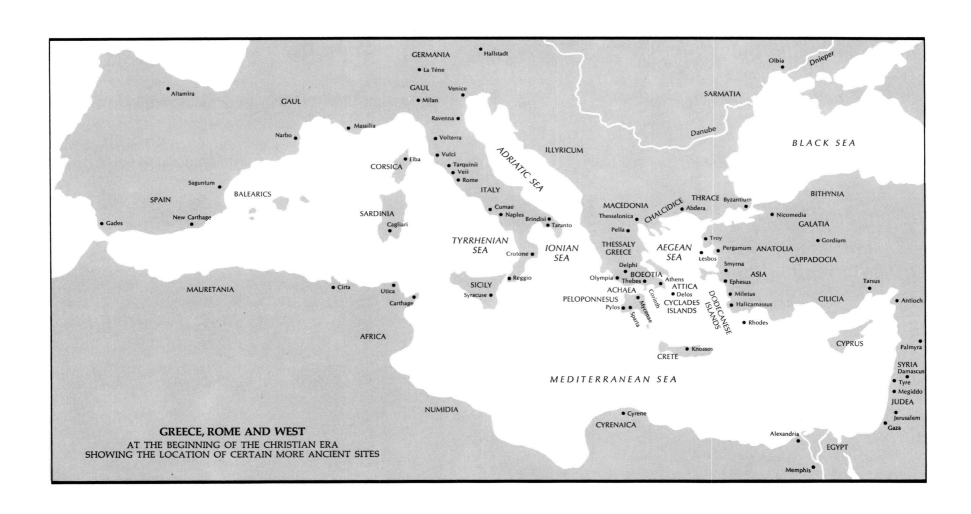

GERMANIA
• Hallstadt
• La Téne
GAUL • Venice
GAUL • Milan
• Ravenna
Narbo • Massilia
• Volterra
CORSICA • Elba • Vulci
• Tarquinii
• Veii
• Rome
ITALY
Altamira
SPAIN BALEARICS
Saguntum
Gades • New Carthage
SARDINIA
Cagliari
TYRRHENIAN SEA
ADRIATIC SEA
ILLYRICUM
Cumae
• Naples
Brindisi
• Taranto
MACEDONIA
Thessalonica
Pella
THRACE
CHALCIDICE Byzantium
Abdera
SARMATIA
Olbia Dnieper
Danube
BLACK SEA
BITHYNIA
• Nicomedia
GALATIA
• Gordium
MAURETANIA
• Cirta
Utica
Carthage
AFRICA
IONIAN SEA
Crotone
SICILY
Syracuse
• Reggio
THESSALY
GREECE
Delphi
Olympia • Thebes
ACHAEA
PELOPONNESUS
Pylos
Sparta
Mycenae
BOEOTIA
Athens
ATTICA
Corinth
Delos
CYCLADES
ISLANDS
AEGEAN
SEA
Lesbos
Troy
Pergamum
Smyrna
ASIA
Ephesus
Miletus
Halicarnassus
DODECANESE
ISLANDS
Rhodes
ANATOLIA
CAPPADOCIA
CILICIA
Tarsus
• Antioch
CYPRUS
CRETE
• Knossos
MEDITERRANEAN SEA
NUMIDIA
• Cyrene
CYRENAICA
Alexandria
EGYPT
Memphis
Palmyra
SYRIA
Damascus
• Tyre
• Megiddo
JUDEA
Jerusalem
Gaza

GREECE, ROME AND WEST
AT THE BEGINNING OF THE CHRISTIAN ERA
SHOWING THE LOCATION OF CERTAIN MORE ANCIENT SITES

We now cross into Europe. Aboriginal evidence of man's early existence on the continent abounds, but his civilization deferred interminably to the Near East. From late Paleolithic times he attempted forms of artistic expression. His Magdalenian phase is testament to a highly developed technique in cave painting and the fashioning of artifacts. In addition to the well-publicized sites such as Altamira, Dordogne, Lascaux, Petersfels, and Dolni Vestonice, his Ice Age creations have been found in practically every country in Europe south of Latitude 52°. The subject matter suggests that they were conceived with magical intent. Still, much of our own modern sacerdotalism and religious dogma perpetuates hoary superstition.

The *Aegean* civilization which arose in the myriad islands of the Aegean Sea was the first high culture to penetrate Europe. Crete was settled early by Mediterranean tribes, who, well before 3500 B.C., occupied all of the Aegean archipelago. Notice on the map how Crete in addition to forming an easy stepping stone to Asia and Africa virtually forms a lake of the Aegean. To the south a couple of hundred miles lies Egypt, to the east much closer lies Asia Minor, crossed by roads leading to the Fertile Crescent. So the older Oriental civilizations converged upon the Aegean by two routes. Hence, it was the Aegean *Islands*, not the mainland, which served as an incubator for the first European civilization.

These early folk are called Aegeans although the term is geographical, not racial. They subsequently spread to the mainland of Greece and the contiguous littoral of Asia Minor. But the fountainhead of Aegean culture remained on Crete. By 2000 B.C. the island people had become highly civilized. They learned the art of pictographic writing which they developed into their more convenient indigenous linear script. A benign climate and fruitful soil bountifully sustained their agriculture and animal husbandry. Their skill in metalurgy and the manufacture of beautifully decorated egg shell ceramics created a monopolistic trade throughout the Mediterranean. And they built ships to carry their goods and warships to protect them. So they became the great maritime power. It followed that the Aegean world grew very wealthy. A line of Cretan sovereigns built splendid palaces at Knossos and Phaestus. They were arranged in the Egyptian manner but were without the great protecting walls, indicating that Crete was internally peaceful and ex-

ternally secure. Her ships were the island battlements, and we still speak of the sea-kings of Crete.

Crete's *Minoan* thalassocracy, named for mythical King Minos, reached its height at about 1600 B.C. Sir Arthur Evans' reconstruction of the Palace of Knossos, possibly over-imaginative, shows colonnaded halls, fine stairways, and impressive areas, representing the first real architecture in Europe. The palace fresco-painted walls suggest Nilotic influences, but they are aquiver with movement—emancipated. These walls were adorned with spectacular glazed figures. The dawn of that spirit which afterwards animated Hellenic art is seen in Minoan art's approach to realities (No. 61). Noble vases, powerful and impressive, belong amongst the finest works ever produced by any people—the Cretan sculptor in ivory, the goldsmith, and the artificer in bronze wrought masterpieces!

These highly sophisticated Minoans appear to have lived in a whirl of pleasure and luxury. The Cretan world is reminiscent of Versailles with its elegancies, court fashion arbiters, décolleté, pastoral artificiality, games, fetes, and dances. Excavations substantiate the legends of the Labyrinth, marked with the double ax (Labrys.) Is the fable of Theseus and Ariadne truth? Modern rodeo and circus performers declare that it is impossible, but we have paintings and statues of Minoan youth who seized the horns of huge bulls and somersaulted over their heads. Incredible sport or religion?

So, now simultaneously with the two older centers of civilization on the Nile and in Mesopotamia, a third great civilization flourished in this world of Crete as it shook off western lethargy to form a cultural link between the east and dormant Europe. The adjacent mainland, both in Europe and Asia Minor, continued to lag behind the islands.

A digression: it is astonishing that for thousands of years the annals of the beginnings of western man's civilization were regarded as myths. Only during the last fifty years have many legends become substantiated facts. As late as 1870 no one believed that civilized people had ever lived in Europe prior to the Greeks who had universally been credited with authoring western civilization. The discoverer of the Aegean culture was the brilliant Heinrich Schliemann. He excavated at Hissarlik (Troy), at Mycenae, and he founded the site of Knossos on which Evans spent a rewarding lifetime. A reading of Schliemann is fascinating.

Returning to continuity, as early as the beginnings of the third millennium B.C. island people migrated to the Greek mainland and established settlements. This is Evans' hypothesis. They probably mingled their blood with that of the hypothetical Pelasgians. Early Greek vitality was surely due to the diversified genes imparted by its immigrants. Certainly also, Greek blood was tinctured with that of Anatolians, Celts, Urnfield people, Illyrians, Persians, and others.

In the Near East section we watched the invading Indo-European peoples conquer the highland zone, the Fertile Crescent, and finally even Egypt. Theirs was not the invasion of a foreign army which generally withdraws eventually. These were permanent migrations. Other Indo-Europeans, whom we now call *Greeks*, had been drifting toward the Aegean area since before 1800 B.C. They were crude herdsmen, unable to write and with only the rudiments of a civilization. Gradually their vanguard pushed through fertile Thessaly and into the Peloponnesus.

The first Greeks who thus entered southern Greece were the *Achaeans* who seem to have amalgamated with the native population. Exposed as they were to further barbarian migrations from the north they dared not live without protecting walls. So their kings and princes of Homeric type dwelt in Cyclopean palace-citadels on hilltops at Mycenae, with its famed Lion Gate, and at Tiryns. These were the earliest stone castles in Europe. Then also were built the proudest of the beehive tombs. The period between 1600 and 1200 B.C. is known as the *Mycenaean* Age. The term Helladic is also used to designate this mainland culture. It definitely differed from the island culture. The Mycenaean Greeks were addicted to beards. The Cretans were even buried with their razors. So that alone should lay the ever recurrent speculations of a homogenous original Cretan-Mycenaean civilization!

Mycenaeans also established themselves in Miletus, Rhodes, Cyprus, and in Crete itself. They traded with Egypt and the Phoenician towns. This was the inaugural period of Phoenician trade, previously discussed, which eventuated in Phoenician merchantry for a time becoming heir to the entire Mediterranean trade. Archaeology has found surviving in Mycenaean palaces and tombs triumphs of imported Egyptian and Cretan art to attest to high refinements of living.

But this high civilization never extended past a narrow coastal fringe. Cyprus (Nos. 65, 67)—ancient Cuprus—whose rich mines gave the name to copper, was long the eastern outpost. Inertness prevailed inland. For another thousand years settlements and villages stretching northward and westward far across Europe were to remain Neolithic. A few traders from the enlightened areas discussed traversed the river routes. They traveled up the Danube and down the Rhine to the North Sea, or, turning southward, followed the Rhone. They bartered shining beads and pottery and, most important, daggers and ax-heads made of the unknown substance, bronze. At about 2000 B.C. tin had been discovered in Bohemia, and the earliest independent Bronze Age culture on the continent of Europe developed. Thence it spread widely, just as agriculture and cattle breeding had done long before. Notwithstanding this important Danubian development, the Bronze Age peoples of Europe did not advance to a higher civilization.

Another digression before returning to our tortuous tale: the term *Cycladic* is applied to the marbles (No. 62) and pottery of the third and second millennia B.C. emanating from the Cyclades Islands but apparently bears no relation to the Minoan-Hellenic culture.

At about 1500 B.C. the warlike *Dorians*, a second wave of Indo-Europeans, descended from the north. They subdued their kinsmen, the Achaean Greeks, and the indigenous Aegean countrymen. They not only subjugated the mainland but passed over to Crete where they crushed civilization, and the great Cretan palaces went up in flame and smoke. Allegedly they initially infiltrated the island and at first destroyed only Knossos. But events leading up to this remain unclear, and Professor Leonard R. Palmer is currently making a meticulous reappraisal of certain of Sir Arthur Evans' conclusions. By 1000 B.C. the incursions of the barbarian Greek tribes engulfed Hellas, the islands, and the Anatolian coast—the *Dorians* in the south, the *Ionians* in the middle, and the *Aeolians* in the north.

Troy is only a footnote to history, immortalized by Homer. A few miles from the Hellespont is a hill called Hissarlik (Turkish—"place of fortresses"). It commands the approaches to the Dardanelles. This mound offers a prime example of archaeological stratigraphy as the ruins of ten identifiable cities lie buried in layers beneath it. Blegen places the earliest level as from about 5000 years ago. Strata 7-A, destroyed about 1200 B.C., is Homer's Ilium—Troy (No. 63). Virgil's *Aeneid* owes much to Homer. At any rate, although there has been nothing of Troy visible above ground for 2500 years, thanks to Homer it became a hallowed shrine. The conquerors Xerxes, Alexander the Great, Julius Caesar, Napoleon, and others all made pilgrimages to the region. The site has repeatedly been excavated. Schliemann located the Palace of Priam but failed to recognize it when he found the pre-Mycenaean treasure. Recently we visited a Turkish archaeological expedition working there.

Historically the rulers of Troy were rich commercial kings. Their castle-fortress, rebuilt many times by many conquering new landlords of many races, was a thousand years older than the citadel at Mycenae. Homeric Trojans were people from Thrace and Macedonia who had originally been driven east by the Illyrians and who had dispossessed the western Hittites. These Trojans in the Aegean were the Greeks' commercial rivals. Cynical perhaps, but were the Trojan Wars a tribute to Sparta's fair Helen or merely a trade war for control of the Dardanelles?

In the previous section we traced the cataclysmic events which attended the transition from the Bronze to the Iron Age around 1200 B.C. in the Near East. There, the pitiless Assyrians desolated the Fertile Crescent, the Hittites were obliterated, and Egypt decayed in the nerveless hands of Ikhnaton. The chaos of a dark age followed. In the Aegean area at approximately the same time the predatory movement of displaced races overthrew order. The Mycenaean Greeks, fatally weakened, succumbed to the barbarians. At this early date another example of the interdependency of nations!

The period of catastrophe cannot be attributed wholesale to the Dorian invasions. Turbulence to the northeast and in the Levant caused the vast, enigmatic migrations of the so-called Sea Peoples. Of the complex situation on Crete, there is a strong presumption that before 1200 B.C. a Mycenaean military dynasty was already in control. Displaced Cretans fled to Palestine and became the Biblical Philistines.

The following is not peripheral economic speculation. Mycenaean population had been extraordinarily dense. Southern Greece could not grow enough food to be self-supporting. She depended upon grain from Egypt and the Black Sea area and metal from abroad in reciprocal exchange for her raw materials and manufactured goods. And this was barter, as there was little medium of exchange, as coinage. The two classic principles of Greek survival, even then,

were emigration and importation. So with the disruption of sea trade, and deprived of invigorating foreign contacts, the Mycenaeans drifted into sterility with a drastic loss of population. Barbarians sacked Mycenae and Tiryns. Even writing was forgotten. Ravaged by plague, invasion, and the burning of cities, Hellas lost contact with her Mycenaean patrimony.

The darkness which shrouded the end of the Bronze Age was a prelude to a brighter dawn. Economic recovery set in as the Phoenicians by sea and the Aramaeans by land contributed to the revival of long distance trading. The *Greeks* emerged to become exponents of the noblest lesson in civilized living ever given to the world. Nevertheless they were the most complex, inconsistent, individualistic people in all history. Philosophers, they were also born politicians with fierce jealousies. Competition was the law of their being and indiscipline their method. Mutual slaughter was more common than mutual understanding. Formulators of ethics, as we follow their history we shall see that those who best served them they destroyed . . . Miltiades, Themistocles, Aristides, Socrates, and even Pericles. Private interest was always of more importance than the general good. Greece later perished because her cities could not federate. Greece, brilliant, never became politically mature.

If we wish to understand her cultural achievements, we might glance at the characteristics of her two predominant tribes—the Dorians and the Ionians. The Dorians were mountain people—practical, hardy, and extremely conservative. The Spartan nobles were descended in a direct line from the Dorians. But Sparta never evolved. She would have no more to do with trade or colonization than with the vainglories of art and literature. The whole of life in Sparta was subordinate to military needs. Her business was war. Her helots were state serfs, and then there were the slaves. But the Spartan was spartan.

The Ionians inhabited the sea coasts and were seafarers, merchants, and cosmopolitans, probably temperamental, surely imaginative. They provided the intellectual element of the blend. Athens, less than 100 miles from Sparta, was its antithesis. Athens lived for trade. To regard Athens only as a liberal democracy, rich in ennobling and perilous lessons for humanity, is to shut our eyes to other aspects of the city. It grew as the result of hard work on the part of craftsmen, potters, smiths, fishermen, and her farmers, and her sailors. The silver from the mines of Mt. Laurium contributed immeasurably to the wealth of Athens. Her penal code, drawn up by Draco, is remarkable less for its harshness than for its equity. Her Pericles was the champion of democratic imperialism. Athens remains an inspiration for mankind, for what the Acropolis represents, for liberty, for equality, and despite defects, for the clime which produced her great sons.

It seems certain that every Greek city was, in its earliest phase, monarchic. At first there were hundreds of these city-kingdoms. Then the four district regions of the mainland each accomplished a union of its city-states—Sparta and Corinth on the Peloponnesus, on the Attic peninsula Athens, and to its north in Boeotia, Thebes assumed leadership without wholly subduing its strong neighbor cities. The result was more loose associations than nations—each jealous of its prerogatives.

Then arose a class of hereditary nobles—large landowners called Eupatrids. With leisure for continual exercise in the use of arms, they were protectors for the state. But they were continual marauders on their own account. Accustomed to the sea, they coasted from harbor to harbor, plundering and burning, to return home laden with rich spoil. Piracy at last became the common calling of the nobles. The power of this noble class eliminated the kings.

Traditionally the Greek Assembly had been a muster of all the weapon-bearing men of the tribes. Now the common man had lost his voice. He also lost his scanty fields, or still worse, was sold into slavery to discharge his debts. To escape the oppressive rule of the nobles, many Greeks emigrated. Colonization is the key to this early phase of Greek history.

Thus Greeks settled the area girdling the Black Sea (Pontus), later to become the granary of Greece. There was expansion along the southern coast of Asia Minor—the Ionian cities (Nos. 64, 66). Greeks were permitted a trading city on the Nile Delta, the predecessor of Alexandria. Libyan Cyrene was founded. Most important, Greeks spread westward across the north Mediterranean shores. Their towns fringed Italy from the heel until well north of present Naples where they were stopped by Etruscan settlements. This came to be known as Magna Graecia and achieved a homogenous civilization. They founded Massilia (Marseilles) and even spread to Spain (Nos. 76, 77). And Greek merchant ships and triremes plied the Mediter-

ranean. Greek colonizers even wrested eastern Sicily from the Phoenicians. But remember, facing this new, semi-civilized, Indo-European, western Mediterranean world at about 750 B.C. was the Semitic-Phoenician empire of Carthage. These rivals repeatedly collided. The growth of Greece and later Rome would decide who would prevail.

Faced with Phoenician trade competition, the work of Greek craftsmen soon surpassed that of their Oriental teachers. Their factories grew, and by 600 B.C. industrial slave labor became an important part of Greek life. No total figures are available, but there can be no doubt that in the thousand years between 600 B.C. and A.D. 400 the Greeks and Romans between them disposed of several million men, women, and children as slaves. This was condoned, although it was recognized as evil. Business was very greatly simplified by the introduction of coined money. Sequentially a prosperous industrial and commercial middle class arose and demanded a voice in the government. And the plight of the peasant on his inexorably sterile land grew more desperate. Political power and the possession of land were still the appanage of the nobility. Then the business middle class evicted the feudal lords, and the privileges of wealth were substituted for those of birth. But the people were still unsatisfied. Social strife became common. Single individuals arose as arbiters. They were called tyrants—but the word did not have the connotation we now place upon it, meaning no more than "master." Tyranny, born of a people to whom indiscipline was endemic, could not long endure. The masses overturned the tyrants.

Democracy triumphed, hailed as the ultimate in political evolution. The people forgot the precept enunciated in ancient days by Odysseus that "the government of the many is never good." They grew drunk on freedom, on argument, and on talk. This was the age of particularism which produced masterpieces but paved the way for disaster. However, Greek democracy remained curiously oligarchic.

Political development in the Greek world offers a striking contrast to that which we found in the ancient Near East. There, city-states finally were united into large and powerful nations. Here, these political microcosms remained apart. They even developed quite divergent customs and language differences. But despite all their variances they recognized the bond of common language, religious beliefs, the oracle at Delphi. All participated in their great national festivals—the Olympic, Isthmian, Nemean, and Pythian games. They regarded themselves as one people—Hellenes. Our word "Greek" itself is but a Latinized version of *Graiei*, one of the first tribes to build a Greek city on Italic soil.

No purpose would be served by our following the history of Greek cities devoured by mutual envy sporadically fighting for a temporary supremacy. Sparta, thanks to her army, early established suzerainty over the Peloponnesus; Athens, with her fleet, in the Aegean.

The year was 500 B.C. Persia had observed the awakening of freedom in Greece. She had put down a revolt of Greeks in her own Ionian cities. They appealed to the Greek motherland to lift their yoke, and Darius decided to punish these presumptuous people. Persia's vast fleets and professional army would surely efface the civic-militia of Greece. Only Sparta had a professional army. Also, even with this gravest peril threatening from without, the Greeks were incapable of calling a truce to their passion for dissidence. They refused to accept unity of command. Some of them talked separate peace. Persia's colossal war machine would surely efface this pigmy.

But Persia failed. On the plain of Marathon, which has remained forever famous, the Athenians repulsed the invader. But victory merely delayed the peril. Xerxes, son of Darius, returned to the charge. He forced the pass of Thermopylae, but the "walls of wood" (Greek ships) held at Salamis; Plataea and Mycale ensured victory. Why? Was the pigmy morally, intellectually superior to the giant? Western man owes a daily debt to these victories.

The period following the Persian Wars was followed by another century and a half in which Greek fought Greek. Athenian ascendancy provoked the opposition of Sparta and Corinth, which led to the Peloponnesian War. The Athenian empire was destroyed. But in vain were the attempts by Sparta and Thebes to dominate Greece.

However, the conclusion of the Persian Wars ushered in the greatest period of Greek history. Athens in particular experienced a surge of cultural development unequaled in world history. Prosperity came with the aid of the Delian League. The Age of Pericles was one of glory. Drama and poetry, art, architecture, and philosophy flourished, and Greece became the fountainhead of all later western civilization. She created it. The list of great men whose words still echo is astonishing, and the list continued to grow even after political misfortune had set in—Aeschylus, Sophocles, Euripides, Aristophanes,

Phidias, Socrates, Plato, and Aristotle. Science, as we know it, first appeared—Archimedes, Hippocrates, Euclid. Eratosthenes calculated the circumference of the earth quite accurately—only a bit later. Shades of Galileo.

The sources of history of Greek mythology are the subject of much conjecture. Even in Homer's time, when gods were pictured anthropomorphically, no code of ethics or morals was connected with them. There was basic animism, complicated by confusion with local deities. The cults of mortal heroes were common from earliest times. Later, heroes and gods became inextricably mixed in legends. We shall not go into the pantheon. Mysteries such as Eleusinian, Orphic, and Dionysian were important for their strong ethical and moral teachings, and their priests were exalted, as were those of the great oracles. By the V century B.C. the faded literal belief in gods enabled poets and philosophers to depict a cosmos wherein moral struggle was paramount.

A most rewarding travel experience is a visit to Greek architectural ruins extant, especially in Asia Minor. Remember that color and gilding were used upon sculpture and architectural elements to accent various portions of buildings. This must have enhanced their harmony and effectiveness (No. 73). No human architecture has ever been more flawlessly lovely. Through the orders we can trace its evolution: Doric—the purest; Ionic—the lightest; Corinthian—the most elegant. All stone and terra cotta sculpture was painted, either wholly or in part (No. 69). Another general Greek practice was the employment of accessories in different materials—eyes inlaid with colored stone, glass, and ivory; metal curls, diadems, wreathes, necklaces, earrings, spears, and the bridles of horses. Greek bronzes (No. 72) were left in their natural, golden yellow color; the patinas with which they are now covered are due to the action of time.

Mycenaean and Greek art are fundamentally different. While there was not the definite cultural cleavage once envisaged by archaeologists, a slow emergence of geometric scheme with linear patterns replaced the curvilinear design and the naturalistic representations of the plant and marine life that had been popular with Minoans and Mycenaeans. Hence, the span from the XI to the VIII century the dominant artistic form during the Archaic Period (625-480 B.C.), B.C. is known as the Geometric Period (No. 70). About two hundred years later, interest in representation arose. Sculpture flowered as with statues of the nude walking youth (*kouros*) and the draped female (*kore*) suggesting Egyptian prototypes and Near Eastern influence. The Early Classical Period (480-450 B.C.) tried to find a balance between naturalism and abstraction. The Classical Period (450-400 B.C.) aimed to represent the ideal human, both in form and character. Significant sculptures from this period are from the Athenian Acropolis. In the Late Classical Period (460-330 B.C.) the emphasis is on emotion, especially in the work of Scopas. Recall Praxiteles, Myron, Lysippus, Timotheus. Unfortunately, painting, and it was surely superb, has not survived except in the treasury of vase decoration (No. 71) portraying both scenes of mythical and mundane life. We know Apollodorus, Zeuxis, Parrhasius, and Appeles. Ancient Hellenism gave way to the Hellenistic civilization (330-100 B.C.) which was the wide-spread Greek-tinctured culture that grew out of the efforts of Alexander the Great to spread Hellenism with his conquests across the known world (No. 75). Many of today's most familiar masterpieces, including Venus of Milo, Dying Gaul, and Nike of Samothrace, are of this epoch. Alas, the majority of Greek originals have disappeared in the lime kiln and the melting pot.

The Greeks had deprecated the archaic, semi-barbarian, hereditary monarchy to their north in the mountains, the grazing grounds and the forest of *Macedonia*. But an ambitious king came to the throne of this mongrel Balkan area, an agglomeration of Thracians, Illyrians, and Epirotes. His name was Philip. He was a great lover of wine, women, horses, and sports. He worked the silver mines of Mount Pangaeus and minted money, which bore his portrait. And this made it possible for him to maintain an army replete with his innovations and to buy men's consciences and the alliance of powerful neighbors. He deliberately undertook an expedition into the Scythian region in 339 B.C. to replenish his then-depleted treasury and returned with 20,000 slaves and much other wealth. Philip of Macedon went from success to success. In vain did Demosthenes sound the call to arms. At Chaeronea in 338 B.C. Philip crushed the combined armies of Athens and Thebes. Corinth opened its gates. The Spartan possessions were mutilated. At last Greece became unified but in the interests of the foreign Macedonian.

Have we dwelt inordinately on Greece? Here a relatively small group of men dethroned the blind and unpredictable deities of the east, which had fettered the world for thousands of years. The Greeks fought their way through the tangled oriental misconceptions to the conviction that the universe is ordered and that men can comprehend it. The Greeks recognized the concepts of virtue and ethics. The Greeks were the first to crystallize the goal of scientific truth. To them we owe our ideas of political freedom and equality before the law. This bedrock of classic civilization at the very beginning of European thought, this intellectual miracle that was Greece, forms our indispensable basis for understanding the present.

From this point we shall use a broad brush as we epitomize the ensuing familiar tale. One of the most romantic figures of antiquity was Philip's son, Alexander the Great. At age nineteen he ascended his father's throne, and upon his death, only fourteen years later, he had attained the widest conquests of ancient times. This young, half-barbarian turned the world upside down, but he revealed to it the splendors of Hellenism. He consolidated Greece, humbled decadent Persia, defeated Lydia, Syria, and Egypt, took Babylon, and broke through the line of the Indus. Possessed of military and administrative genius, the brevity of his meteoric career precluded his consolidation of his conquests. His legacy was too large for his successors, and the fragments of his empire became the booty of his generals, known as the Diadochi.

We must now focus on the Italian Peninsula, as world leadership shifts from the eastern to the western Mediterranean. Less than one hundred miles north of the flat campagna on which lies Rome, we enter more rugged Tuscany, which still bears the name of a near-mythic race of hot-blooded people—the *Etruscans*. Theirs was the first civilization to develop the boot of Italy. The Etruscans were not indigenous to Italy. They were followers of an Asiatic, revealed religion, which bound them together. Their women occupied a privileged place in society, in contrast to the seclusion of the Greek women. This, and a considerable number of linguistic and archaeological facts, buttress the argument that the Etruscan roots lie in Asia Minor, probably Lydia. The end of the VIII century B.C. marks the known emergence of the Etruscans in their Italian coastal cities, succeeding the earlier Villanovan settlements of the Iron Age. Their prosperity developed with amazing rapidity. They exploited the iron and copper mines which abound in upper Etruria and fashioned durable weapons and wares for barter. The VII and VI centuries B.C. were the period of wealth, power, and expansion for Etruria.

Despite their obscurities and mysteries, the actual life and civilization of the Etruscans are brilliantly illuminated for us by the writing of the ancients and, above all, by the immense pictorial documentation of their tombs. These tomb paintings are a unique treasure as virtually all painting of the classic world before Imperial Rome has vanished. D. H. Lawrence, in his fine book *Etruscan Places*, waxes lyric over these spontaneous frescoes. Of course, most of the tombs were pillaged in antiquity of all movable treasure of gold and sculpture and jewelry.

In the Etruscan archaeological field, a salute is due that passionate amateur Italian archaeologist Carlo M. Lerci, whose work we have witnessed. His techniques with potentiometers and aerial cameras which he uses to locate tombs, and his employment of an earth borer and periscope-equipped camera to photograph the interior of these tombs before excavation, is revolutionary.

Little is left of Etruscan cities above ground—a few imposing walls, some gates. But the tombs were built in the image of the Etruscan house, and they were furnished and stocked for an after-life. They contain plastic art, rich and diversified. This art reveals the Greek and Roman influences that first nourished, then ultimately destroyed, the Etruscans. Bucchero black-ware, stone sculpture in the round, and bas reliefs display bold stylization rather than harmony of form (No. 87). Late portraiture is excellent. We are especially attracted to the dynamic bronzes, frequently greatly elongated (Nos. 83, 85, 86, 88).

As foes and, indeed, one-time rulers of Rome, the Etruscans were regarded by the Romans with respect, but this attitude was tinctured by disdain for their uninhibited and luxurious way of life, which the Romans thought decadent. But they were sufficiently virile to resist Rome for hundreds of years. The Battle of Cumae (474 B.C.), celebrated by Pindar, when Greek fighting ships denied them the seas, foreshadowed their eclipse. In the IV century B.C. the inroads of the Celts weakened the Etruscans, and the Romans ended the independence of this vigorous race.

The history of *Rome* begins with a bridge. A thousand years before Christ, coast marshes extended for a dozen miles above the mouth of the River Tiber to where the river is obstructed by a small island.

Here a bold hill guarding the river crossing was crowned by a stronghold. Here, once a year gathered the Latin tribes, united for a feast to their chief god, Jupiter. And here was built the bridge. Priests guarded the sanctity of this bridge and supervised its cults. One of these priests was the bridge-maker, even then called the pontifex. Giacomo Boni and others have excavated these earliest evidences of man in the Forum—his ancient necropolis, his stables, and mud huts. The seven hills of Rome are now partially flattened by the erosion of time, but we know that the Latin tribes—Albans on the Palatine and Capitoline—warred against the Sabines on the Quirinal precisely as man has always fought. And, as always, peace came, and the dank marshes below the hills were drained. The center of the marsh became the communal marketplace for the straggling villages—the Forum. From mud huts were the beginnings of the Eternal City.

By 750 B.C. a line of Etruscan kings arrogated control of the villages which gradually merged into the city of Rome. But the population of Latium continued to be Latin and to speak the Roman tongue, although Roman civilization became essentially Etruscan. Etruscans introduced improvements including art, architecture, religion, and organization which have lasted until our times.

The Etruscan kings were driven from Rome at about 500 B.C. Then from among the nobles, called "patricians," the people, called the "plebes" (plebian), elected two "consuls." And this new state we must call a "republic." Abuses by the consuls resulted in the patricians allowing the plebes to elect a group of new officials, the "tribunes," with veto powers. Then, as a result of bloodless evolution, the differences between the patricians and the plebes were resolved during the first few hundred years of the republic under the influential Senate, which initially provided wise and stable leadership. For many centuries, only when the safety of Rome itself was in great jeopardy, were full powers very temporarily relinquished to a dictator chosen by the consuls. The Senate was Rome—S.P.Q.R.

Early Roman policy was in striking contrast to the narrowness of Greece and of the Etruscans. Unity became her greatest strength. Two centuries after the expulsion of the Etruscan kings the little republic on the Tiber was mistress of all Italy. But in the new territories gained she planted colonies of her citizens and granted Roman citizenship and privileges to the assimilated populations. This agricultural expansion policy, steadily and consistently followed by the

Senate, was irresistible. Rome acquired an ever-increasing body of brave and hardy citizen-soldiers, cultivating their own lands and ever ready to take up the sword in defense of the state.

The first threat to the survival of the infant republic was the Etruscans, soon eliminated. Then the barbarian Indo-European *Celtic* nomads thoroughly sacked the city in 390 B.C., but they withdrew after the payment of a ransom of gold. A hundred years later Tarentum and the other Greek colonies fringing southern Italy and Sicily, alarmed at the threatening expansion of Roman power, called upon their Greek homeland for assistance. The last of the great Greek generals, Pyrrhus, answered the summons and repeatedly routed the Romans. In fact, the gallant Pyrrhus gained so many victories over Romans that he, himself, was completely exhausted and his army depleted. To this day an overcostly triumph is known as a "Pyrrhic" victory. So he finally departed, leaving the hapless Greek cities to surrender and accept alliance with the Romans. The ships of Phoenician Carthage had contributed to Pyrrhus' woes.

Before the discouraged Pyrrhus wended his way home, he made a most interesting prophecy: he foretold the dreadful struggle later to ensue between Rome and Carthage. To quote: "What a battlefield I am bequeathing to Rome and Carthage." The riches from the vast booty of this war, though, enabled Rome to bring good fresh water to the city. The arches of large sections of the most famous aqueduct in the world, the Roman Aqueduct, thirty-four miles long, wrought by a people on the ascendant, continues to amaze us today after 2,200 years.

The *Carthaginians* were Punians, the same people whom we already know as Phoenicians, descendants of the Semites of Canaan. In the III century B.C. Carthage was the wealthiest city in the world (No. 84). Through the warehouses of Carthage passed the gold and pearls of the east, purple from Tyre, ivory and skins from the African interior, incense from Arabia, linen from Egypt, ceramics and aromatic wines from Greece, copper from Cyprus, silver from Spain, tin from England, iron from Elba. Carthage had business corporations, shipping, "banknotes," tall blocks of apartments and office buildings, arsenals, elephants for war, and a huge fleet. She was a plutocracy with implicit faith in the power of gold. Here, small children were regularly sacrificed to a colossal bronze statue of the god Moloch, from whose arms they disappeared into a fiery furnace amid the plaudits of fanatical worshippers.

The Romans had made great advances in arms and tactics over the classic Hellenistic art of war. Her phalanx was now mobile. The military discipline and training of her centurians in the legions surpassed all previous standards of the ancient world. Powerful Carthage had throttled the external trade requisite for Rome's economic survival. Whatever the risk involved, Rome was convinced war could not be avoided. She built a fleet and with the aid of a novel boarding bridge, won the naval battle of Mylae using her soldiers at sea. The three celebrated Punic Wars, which covered a span of 119 years, were ultimately fought between Carthage and Rome. The dreadful bloodletting began in 264 B.C. Hannibal, with his African elephants, held Rome at bay. But by 146 B.C. it was over. Cato concluded his every speech with "Carthage must be destroyed." She was mercilessly extirpated, stone from stone. Carthage and Spain, her European foothold, became Roman provinces.

Rome's struggle for existence was now over. But her people had developed a taste for conquest. Treasure had poured in on them. Slaves and land were theirs for the plucking. A dishonest diplomacy served the interests of a new imperialism. She assimilated Illyria. By 146 B.C. Rome reduced now-decadent Greece to a political cipher. But the triumph of Rome meant the Roman absorption of Hellenistic culture, not its extinction. Numidia, Syria, and Asia Minor fell. Romans adventured as far as the country of the Parthians, those nomads who, moving from their base in Turkestan, had taken over the legacy of Iran and Mesopotamia. Rome almost made contact with the Chinese. They did not fail to lay hands on Egypt, where the Hellenism of the Ptolemies had withered. Rome's mastery of the ancient world is too familiar a story to require retelling, too important to allow forgetting. By the dawn of the Christian Era nothing was lacking to the Glory of Rome. So starts decline!

We shall not detail Julius Caesar, or Augustus—who gave his name to an age—or political and social strife, autocracy, Empire, division, anarchy. The Golden Age of Rome was brief. Toynbee reiterates his prognosis for the death of nations. All the symptoms appeared here. Few worthy or outstanding personalities are among the list of truly terrifying figures who guided Rome to disintegration.

Eventually the Roman people depended upon the capital for a

solution to all of their local problems. Government "generosity" impoverished human spirit and robbed Roman citizens of their dignity. Rome, too, finally relied upon mercenary allies. After the inadvertent ruination of the farmers, the business class was destroyed by ever increasing intervention in the private economy, which entrenched a huge bureaucratic cadre. Our present economic experiments are not new. A controlled economy under Domitian, in order to check overproduction, caused the vines to be uprooted. Under Diocletian, in order to combat the cost of living, government decreed maximum prices and wages. But the natural laws of supply and demand refused to be repealed. The insolent luxury of the debilitated giant in decline tempted predacious barbarians who overthrew her. History is redundant with "wooden shoes climbing upstairs, and satin slippers tumbling down."

Rome was cruel, sensual, and licentious, forever insatiable in its boundless passions. Rome was gorgeous and radiant, but often arrogant and pitiless. How could a whole people participate at the Circus Maximus, Flaminius—ad nauseum? The true legacy of Rome is essentially material. *Pax Romana*, what was it? Nothing more than a formula—an expression of innate orderliness. Not only was it an armed peace, but it was a peace created for innumerable wars— offensive wars waged for expansion; defensive wars waged to retain spoils; foreign wars for land, booty, and slaves; internal wars to repress the restlessness of conquered people. Christian worship was tolerated, never embraced, only during the period when Rome's sands were running out. However, all peoples have looked nostalgically back to Rome. Rome had a passion for order. She taught the lesson of "the State." Earlier civilizations had inaugurated a postal service, used coinage, built fine roads, codified laws and customs. However, the traditions and the language of Rome have left a mark upon us which nothing will ever efface.

Mediocre as painters and sculptors, the Romans were excellent architects and even better masons. At the outset, they did not present themselves as belonging to that small group of peoples endowed with a spontaneous capacity for art. Originally all was Etruscan or Greco-Etruscan. They emulated the Etruscans in making permanent the memory of the dead with their "imagines" of wax—later in stone (Nos. 90, 94). Greek modelers were brought to Rome to decorate their buildings (No. 95). Then the conquest of Greece brought Romans into more direct contact with the art of Greece proper. Philhellenism became the ruling fashion of Rome. Wealthy connoisseurs formed collections drawn from the Greek provinces. Even portraiture borrowed an Hellenic character in the time of Caesar. Yet this period saw the beginning of the historical or commemorative method to the development of which the Empire gave so powerful an impulse. Art was enlisted in the service of the Empire (Nos. 91, 92).

This is best illustrated in architecture. The ruins of temples, palaces, baths, coliseums, aqueducts, buildings, and theatres are still mute evidence of Rome's desire to impress at even the most remote outposts of Empire. Envisage fantastic Baalbek, Petra, Ephesus, and a hundred other sites. Most of these were executed in marble and profusely adorned with carving and statuary (No. 89). Another specific achievement of the Roman architect was the application of the arch, the vault, and the dome, originally learned from the Etruscans. The rectilinear, Greek-type buildings gave way to vaulted structures. These later paved the way for medieval and more particularly Romanesque and Gothic styles (Nos. 294 to 297).

The technical dexterity which characterizes early Roman stucco decoration and sculpture in relief or in the round was largely Greek influenced (No. 93). But the content is different as it is associated with new religions and political ideals. Portrait heads show uncompromising realism. Bronzes (No. 98) and occasional lead castings (No. 99) display technical proficiency (No. 97) with few works of greatness (No. 96). Roman art continued its course, scarcely disturbed by a brief renaissance of classicism under Hadrian. The historical reliefs which survive from the Antonine period show the new leaven at work which brought about radical changes in the entire domain of plastic art. Color, rather than form, assumed a peak on the palette of artistic values. Painting, mural, fresco, tempera, and encaustic were attended with conspicuous success; the sister art of mosaic was carried to a high degree of technical perfection (No. 101); and in sculpture, new conventions were dictated by the need for contrasts of light and shadow. By the close of the III century A.D. further transformation had taken place, which coincided with the political revolution whereby the absolute monarchy of Diocletian succeeded the principate of Augustus. Finally, the portraits of the mounted Constantine had dropped all traces of naturalism; they were monumental, both in scale and concept, and their rigid "frontality" carries us back to the primitive art of the east. Again, as in Mesopotamia—impress the populace.*

Each major chapter of history ends in a flood of *barbarians*. To backtrack, we have mentioned those fascinating Indo-European forerunners of the historical nations of western and middle Europe, the *Celts*. Understand that Celt is a generic, not a specific name. One of your grandparents many, many times removed, was probably a Celt. Celtic archaeological remains from the X century B.C. (Urnfield, etc.) are to be found in the Valley of the Danube. By the III century B.C. the Celts had spread in a great arc across western and central Europe and had penetrated into England and Ireland (Albion and Ierne) and Scandinavia. Celts enjoyed periods of almost unchecked banditry. They looted and fought to possess lands. They served as mercenaries for the Greeks. Celts sacked Rome at its beginnings, before settling in the Valley of the Po. Strabo, whose writings are a rich source of knowledge of the ancient world, says of the Celts, "The whole nation . . . is war mad, and both high-spirited and quick for battle, although otherwise simple and not uncouth."

Today Celtic names survive widely in France, Spain, northern Italy, and in the Valley of the Danube. Although the Celts are more the progenitors of most of us than the Latins or Greeks, they are shrouded in popular misconception. Every high school student knows the Gauls. That is a purely Roman name, "Galli," for a segment of the Celts. "Deutsch" means "people" within the philological Teutonic family. "Teutones" is the Latin form of a Celtic word meaning "people." So all non-Celtic intruders in an area might have been called Teutonic. "Germani" was originally the name of a Celtic tribe which achieved a suzerain position. But by this time Gaul had been Romanized. Celts all over Europe had taken roots and were no longer nomadic (No. 100). They are not to be included in the tidal wave about to engulf the civilized world.

Unfortunately, though, Germany's first national hero, Hermann (Arminius) had liberated his country from Rome in A.D. 9. But in so doing he had deprived her of the benefits of a civilization. Germany remained savage for centuries, and the Rhine, which might have

been a great highway of communication, was turned into a sundering moat.

From whence came the great waves of conquering nomads now poised to inundate civilization? In eastern Asia, round the periphery of China, was a constant eddy of Turco-Mongol tribes, the main element of which was Hun. The Alans were squeezed down toward the Caspian and the Caucasus. Further north, spread out along the Baltic coast, lay the Finns, the Lithuanians, and the Slavs. Scandinavia was the home of the Norwegians, Danes, and Swedes. The vast area stretching from the Vistula to the Rhine was peopled by various Germanic groups—the Goths, who had moved down into the Ukraine, the "shining" (or Ostro) Goths to the east, the "wise" (or Visi) Goths to the west. There were Vandals on the Danube, Angles on the Schleswig, Lombards on the banks of the Elbe, Saxons on the Weser, Alamanni on the Main, and a spearhead of Franks and Burgundians on the Rhine. All barbarians, but not all to the same degree, and they ever increasingly coveted the riches of weakening Mistress Rome.

At the beginning of the IV century, the Huns, whom the Han Dynasty, away off in China, had contained for centuries, breached the Great Wall and mastered northern China. Perhaps civilization quickly softened them as other nomad bands, Mongols from Manchuria, dispossessed them. This incident marked a turning point in the history of the world as it initiated the vast human migrations which, according to the distinguished French historian, René Sedillot, made the Great Invasions inevitable.

The Huns, with the Mongols on their heels, swept across Asia. They drove westward all the peoples whom they encountered. They entered Europe and passed the Volga. Leaving the Slavs on their right undisturbed, they crushed the Ostrogoths, who, in turn, streamed toward the Danube and broke into northern Italy. They prized out the Visigoths, who were forced to take refuge, first in Thrace, then in Illyria, whence they moved on into Italy, pillaged Rome, entered Gaul, and halted only when they reached the Atlantic on the coast of Aquitaine. The Alamanni, set in movement by the Huns, pushed the Vandals and Burgundians before them. The Vandals crossed the Rhine, swept through Gaul, and passed into Spain (Vandalusia). and subsequently into North Africa. Later they were to return to pillage in Europe. The Burgundians went no further than Savoy. The

---

*Our thanks to Dr. Dietrich von Bothmer, Curator Greek and Roman Department, Metropolitan Museum of Art, New York City, for reviewing the foregoing section.

Franks, too, in the general surge westward entered northern Gaul. The Saxons and the Angles, when failing Rome withdrew her legions, crossed the channel to Britain. From this great melting pot of peoples came the molten stuff from which the nations of the future were formed. Of course, busily fighting, the barbarian hordes have left us few evidences of their art save for a few rude sculptures, some ornaments, and jewelry.

The domain of the Huns by the middle of the V century extended from the Caucasus to the Seine. Would the hirsute and many-wived warrior Attila, the Scourge of God, ever be contained? But suddenly Atilla died, and the empire of the Huns crumbled and disappeared. But the Huns were to return in different forms to be the terrors of a later Europe—as Bulgars, as Turks, as Mongols. Europe was still to experience Genghis Khan and Tamerlane. For a thousand years the barbarians were yet to be resisted under the solidarity of Christendom until came the time for the hatching of the nations. So we shall depart this history until we return for the reawakening of the west, in the concluding Section VII. Following is the chronology of these people.

EARLY EUROPEAN SYNOPTIC CHRONOLOGY			
CULTURE	APPROXIMATE AREA	APP. PERIOD	CONQUERORS
Frankish	Germanic to most of West and Central Europe	III Cent-IX Cent. A.D.	Treaty of Mersen (870) Kingdom of West Franks became France, East Franks—Germany
Lombard	Germanic to Italy	Pre-History-772 A.D.	Disappeared after Charlemagne
Vandal	Germanic to Gaul (406), Spain, Carthage (439), Rome (455)	Pre-History-533 A.D.	Disappeared after Belisaurius
Visigoth	N. of Black Sea to Rome, S. Gaul & N. Spain	III Cent. B.C.-711 A.D.	Disappeared after Tarik the Moor
Ostrogoth	N. of Black Sea to Hungary and Italy	III Cent. B.C.-552 A.D.	Disappeared after Totila's defeat
Hun	N.E. Asia to China (III Cent.-581) Volga (372), Rome (432)	III Cent. B.C.-451 A.D.	Disappeared after Attila's defeat
Carthaginian	North Africa—Bay of Tunis	IX Cent. B.C.-146 B.C.	Rome
Roman	Italy—Later from Britain to Orient	753 B.C.-476 A.D.	Germanic Nomads, Byzantium
Etruscan	Umbria and part of Latium	800-396 B.C.	Invading Celts, Rome
Celtic (Gallic)	Central and West Europe to British Islands	2000 B.C.-(Flowered 1200-400 B.C.)-51 B.C.	Rome
Greek	Greece, Colonies—Ionian Shores Asia Minor to Sicily, S. Italy, France, Spain	Before 1000-146 B.C.	Rome (After unification by Philip II of Macedon (338)—Hellenistic
Mycenaean	N. and Cen. Peloponnesus, Troy, Cyclades	3000-900 B.C.	Greece
Minoan	Crete	3000-1200 B.C.	Greece
Illyrian	North and East shores of Adriatic	Pre-History-167 B.C.	Rome
Thracian	S.E. Balkan Peninsula, N.E. Greece	Pre-History-III Cent. A.D.	Forced East by Illyria (1300 B.C.), Greece, Rome (I-III Cent. A.D.)

61. MINOAN FIGURINE—PAINTED TERRA COTTA—
CA. 1500 B.C.—H. 13.1 cm. (5⅛″)

This votive figurine is from western Crete (Atsipadhais). My-
cenaean influenced, it exemplifies the beginnings of Aegean
high culture, called Minoan, after the legendary King Minos.
It is painted in a geometric design. The figure resembles the
Greek letter ψ, after which the type is named. Ex. Coll. J. J.
Klejman, New York.

62. CYCLADIC FIGURE—MARBLE—LATE III MILLENNIUM
B.C.—H. 24.5 cm. (9⅝″)

This female idol is of the earliest known original sculptures of
the Bronze Age. The incipient art of the Cyclades Islands in the
southwestern Aegean Sea differed entirely from the nearby
Helladic culture. However, for abstract art it is the peer of the
modern work of Arp, Brancusi, or Picasso. Found on the Island
of Naxos, argillaceous matter adheres to the translucent marble.

63. TROJAN STATUETTE—STEATITE—CA. 1300 B.C.—
H. 10.1 cm. (4″)

A great rarity, this finely modeled figure of a man was excavated at "Level 7A" from the mount of Hissarlik—the ancient
Troy (Ilium)—by the Turkish Archaeological Expedition of
1959 and presented to us. This is the area first dug by Heinrich
Schliemann after 1870. This mount gives validity to the legends of Homer and the site of the Trojan War.

64. IONIAN HORSE—BRONZE—CA. V CENTURY B.C.—H. 6.7
cm. (2⅝″)

This beautiful small classic bronze and No. 66, the lion, were
the only two pieces that we were permitted to take away from
Ephesus. Ephesus is now several miles from the Aegean Sea, although in antiquity it was one of the major Ionian seaports.
Due to the silting up of the river, the sea has receded many
miles. However, its wharves, with rings to hold ships, are now
to be seen inland. We waded through swamp land to view
streets paved in marble, bearing the ruts of chariot wheels.
Beautifully carved marble architectural fragments are every-
where, transcending in beauty and interest much of what is
extant in Greece today.

65. CYPRIOT HORSEMAN—TERRA COTTA—LATE VI CEN-
TURY B.C.—H. 11.5 cm. (4½″)

This archaic horse and rider is representative of similar Cypriot
terra cottas and is of a type which persisted for several centuries. Traces of brown paint.

66. IONIAN LION—BRONZE—CA. V CENTURY B.C.—
H. 4.1 cm. (1⅝″)

This small bronze was found with No. 64 above. Time has been
more unkind to it.

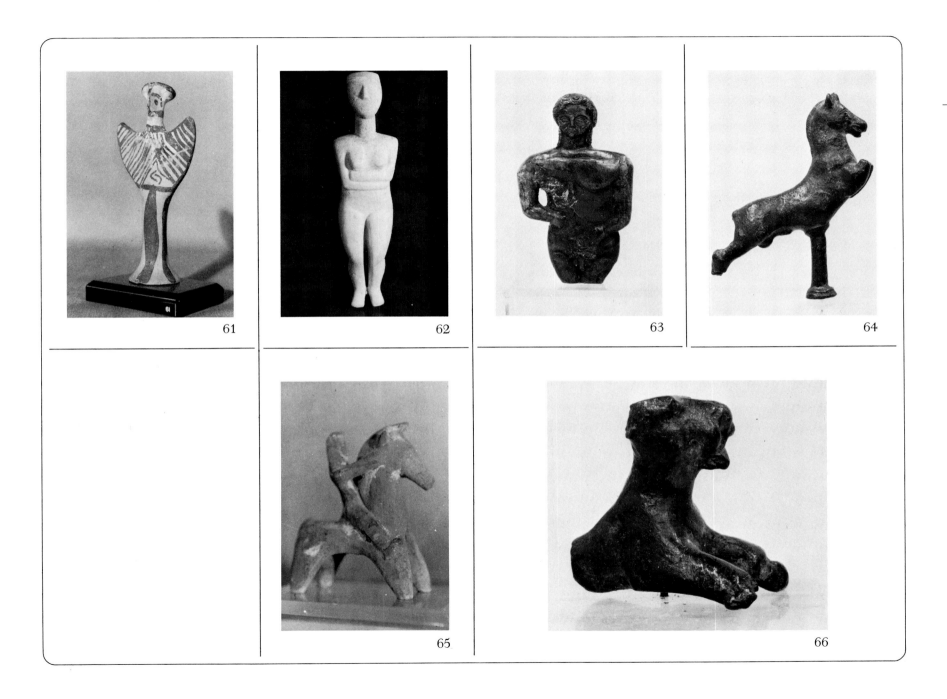

61

62

63

64

65

66

67. CYPRIOT HEAD—LIMESTONE—VI CENTURY B.C.—
H. 15.7 cm. (6¼")

This head of a goddess wearing a floral crown has her face set in the archaic smile of the period. It was unearthed near Paphos on the Island of Cyprus.

68. GRECIAN PANTHER—PENTELIC MARBLE—
IV CENTURY B.C.—L. 27 cm. (10⅝")

Powerful movement is expressed in this fragmentary statuette of the panther. Reported to have been found near Sparta. With gratitude to Mr. Mathias Komor, New York, who has obtained many fine pieces for us over the years. Ex. Coll. Guthrie, Craigie, Scotland.

69. GRECIAN TANAGRA—TERRA COTTA—IV CENTURY
B.C.—H. 24.9 cm. (9¾")

These figures are generally called Tanagras after the cemetery at Tanagra in Boeotia where they were first found. The lofty remoteness of the V century has given way to a purely human charm. The figures are not divinities whose sublimity invokes worship. They represent the people of their time transformed into works of art by their exquisite grace. We do not know their purpose, but the majority have been found in tombs. These terra cottas were also produced at other centers as Myrina, Smyrna, and Tarsus. This woman in a restful pose, quiet and serene, has great delicacy and elegance. Only a trace of the original tempera applied on white engobe remains. The figure is hollow and made from several molds. Authenticated by Miss Gisela N. A. Richter, Metropolitan Museum, New York. Ex. Coll. A. W. Wilson, London.

70. GRECIAN FIGURE—BRONZE—VII CENTURY B.C.—
H. 11.5 cm. (4½")

This early Geometric Period figure of a standing man has a cylindrical, unarticulated body and short, outstretched arms. Eyes, nose, and hair are indicated. Smooth green patina. Similar pieces have been found at Olympia. Ex. Coll. Prof. George Nicole, Geneva.

71. GRECIAN VASE—PAINTED POTTERY—V CENTURY B.C.
—H. 31.7 cm. (12½")

This red figure Attic Lekythose, attributed to the Aischines Painter, depicts a narcistic picture. Published: Beasley's *Attic Red Figure Painters*, Vol. 1, p. 715, No. 178.

72. GRECIAN FIGURE—BRONZE—III CENTURY B.C.—
H. 11.5 cm. (4½")

The feet are missing from this vigorous portrayal of the accoutered Hercules, which shows unusual sculptural detail. Fine dark patina.

67

68

69

70

71

72

73. GRECIAN GRIFFIN—WHITE ARGILLACEOUS MATE-RIAL AND GOLD LEAF—IV CENTURY B.C.—L. 11.5 cm. (4 9/16″)

Situated on the instep of the Italic boot, the Spartan Greek colony city of Tarentum rose to become the first city of Magna Grecia. Here in a burial, was found this finely modeled gilt griffin. It had probably been affixed to a wooden casket through its perforations. Professor Reinhard Lullies, Keeper of the State Collection of Classical Art at Munich, has written a book upon such reliefs.

74. GRECIAN STELE—PENTELIC MARBLE—CA. 320 B.C.—H. 53.6 cm. (21⅛″)

Athens and the triangular mountainous district around it was known as Attica in ancient Greece. The softness and roundness of the late classical ideal were abandoned at the dawn of Hellenistic art. This Attic votive relief, dedicated to the Eleusinian Deities, shows a standing *kore*. The figure wears a chiton and apoptygma girdled under the breast. With one hand she rests a burning torch on the altar and with the other pours a libation from a phiale. The architectural frame is in the shape of an aedicula. The lovely head and erect figure combine to give an effect of grace and dignity.

75. GRECIAN SPHINX—BRONZE—III-II CENTURY B.C.—H. 7.7 cm. (3″)

This graceful, seated, winged sculpture, a cross between a sphinx and a griffin, has a superb patina. Exact Grecian provenance unknown. Ex. Coll. Azeez Khayat, Haifa.

76. IBERIAN FIGURE—BRONZE—VI CENTURY B.C.—H. 10.6 cm. (4⅛″)

Hispanic or Iberian bronzes are seldom seen except in the Archaeological Museum in Madrid. Commerce existing between the Iberians and the Sardinians and Etruscans explains the parallels in their art forms.

77. IBERIAN FIGURE—BRONZE—V CENTURY B.C.—H. 9.2 cm. (3⅝″)

This votive bronze was found in the temple of Collado de Los Jardines—Despeneperros, Spain. Published: *Pantheon*, 1931, p. 251. Ex. Coll. Prof. H. Obermaier, Madrid.

73

74

75

76

77

83. ETRUSCAN CENSER—BRONZE—IV CENTURY B.C.—
H. 41.4 cm. (16¼″)

The Etruscan civilization dominated the Italian peninsula prior to the rise of Rome. Its wealth was predicated upon an early knowledge of metal working. This is a superior example of three legged incense burner. It portrays a standing Aphrodite figure and has four doves around the cup.

84. PUNIC STELE—MARBLE—II CENTURY B.C.—H. 43.3 cm. (17⅛″)

This bas relief was found near the modern Arab village of Sidi-bu-Said in an early II century B.C. cemetery within the perimeter of ancient Punic Carthage. Marble in this area was not indigenous and the theory is that these grave markers were imported, already sculptured, and then inscribed and sold locally. This is borne out by the crudity of the inscription in contrast to the rather fine sculpture. It is incised in "barbaric Greek," logically due to the polyglot commercialism of Carthage. Professor Paul Friedlander of the University of California translated the inscription to read—"African name—Greek name; Sons of Two Greek names: Farewell." So evidently although the sculpture of a male and female figure, two men were buried in a common grave beneath it. This was not unusual.

85. ETRUSCAN STATUE—BRONZE—VI CENTURY B.C.—
H. 18.6 cm. (7⅜″)

This warrior is of the archaic attenuated type. This form, repeatedly used by these people, probably represented the most Latin of the gods, Mars, father of Romulus, agricultural god, and god of war. He wears the great Corinthian style crested helmet, and a perizoma; cuirass and greaves are incised. The holes where he originally carried a spear and shield are visible, but these are missing. The right foot shows restoration. Ex. Coll. Dr. F. Lederer, Berlin.

86. ETRUSCAN STATUETTE—BRONZE—EARLY VI CENTURY B.C.—H. 11.7 cm. (4⅝″)

This standing male dedicatory figure is holding a round object in his right hand. The left arm is missing.

87. ETRUSCAN URN—POLYCHROMED TERRACOTTA—III-II CENTURY B.C.—L. 44.6 cm. (17½″)

The lid of this urn probably depicts the form of the deceased, seen here in repose, her head upon a pillow. The facade on the urn shows a scene of warriors and their shields, with one fighter already lying wounded at the feet of the others. Considerable polychrome remains. This was found at Chiusi in 1911 by Campbell Thompson, the freelance British archaeologist who later worked in Sumer.

88. ETRUSCAN STATUETTE—BRONZE—III CENTURY B.C. —L. 13.6 cm. (5⅜″)

Naked Herakles is shown advancing, brandishing his club; from his outstretched arm hangs the lion's skin. This lively specimen of the well-known type of Etruscan "Ercolino" has a fine greyish green patina. Ex. Coll. Prof. George Nicole, Geneva.

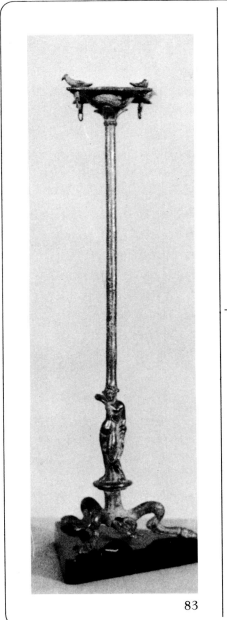

83

84

85

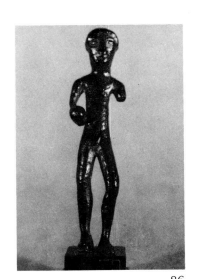

86

87

88

89. ROMAN PLAQUE—PARTIALLY DECOMPOSED MARBLE
—350-400—L. 1 m., 23 cm. (9⅛")

This bas relief came from an ancient private dwelling along the Appian Way outside the Roman city gates near the chapel of Saint Sebastian, underneath which are labyrinths of catacombs. This was all the information available when it was obtained. However, it showed the signs of over 1000 years of weathering. The only clue to the derivation was the bull prominently displayed upon the wall, quite possibly the attribute of St. Sylvester during whose pastorate (314-335) Christianity became the official religion of Rome. The bull relates the legend of Zambria and the conversion of the Emperor Constantine. It was widely represented into the V century.

90. ROMAN SARCOPHAGUS—MARBLE—IMPERIAL PERIOD
—II-III CENTURY—L. 1 m., 69 cm. (66 1/16")

From its size it is evident that this was the sarcophagus of a child. It is interesting to conjecture what child of wealth occupied it until at some time during the past 1700 years he was dispossessed and his resting place usurped for conversion into a bath tub. Ex. Coll. De Motte, London.

91. ROMAN HEAD—MARBLE—I-III CENTURY—
H. 32.2 cm. (12¾")

This head was dug out of the Roman ruins at Alexandria, which had been gutted by fire. Despite cleaning, traces of a holocaust are still discernible. We believe it to represent the Roman Emperor Septimus Severus, who died in 211. Severus was born in North Africa, and his family was under the protection of the god Serapis. Members of his family often appeared in the guise of Serapis, whom this resembles. It was evidently mounted on a building as it is routed for joining.

92. ROMAN MEDALLIONS—GOLD—EARLY IV CENTURY
—D. 5.4 cm. (2⅛")

These medallions, found in the Roman ruins of Tarsus, Anatolia, are probably insignia from the tunic of a Roman Centurian officer. They bear the features of the Caesar, Maximin Daia (305-309). The two coins (92-a), bearing his face, struck during his reign, confirm his identity. The gold "aureus" is extremely rare. The bronze "sesterce" shows Maximin Daia wearing the diadem of the medallions.

93. ROMAN BES—TERRA COTTA—I CENTURY—
H. 16.4 cm. (6½")

This fragment of a Campana relief centers on a facing figure of the Egyptian god, Bes, wearing a diadem, placed between a sphinx and a bearded androsphinx.

94. GRECO-ROMAN FRAGMENT—MARBLE—I CENTURY
B.C.—H. 54.1 cm. (21¼")

This fragment is from a sarcophagus found at Constantinople. Ex. Coll. Dikran Kelekian, New York.

89

90

91

92

92a

94

93

95. ROMAN MASK—MARBLE—II-III CENTURY—
W. 31.2 cm. (12¼")

There are very few examples of the Aeschylus mask with the face behind extant, so this is quite unusual. The development of the theatrical mask is ascribed to Aeschylus. The masks, actually used, were of wood and acoustical and contained a speaking tube to increase the resonance of the voice as the audience was at a considerable distance in the frequently huge outdoor amphitheatres.

96. ROMAN DEER—BRONZE—MODERN CAST OF
I CENTURY ORIGINAL—L. 75.8 cm. (29⅞")

The only reproduction which we feel should be included in this collection is this delightful bronze, cast from the original. It is of the famous deer discovered in the ruins of the house of Pisoni in Herculaneum. The modernity of expression in which this sculpture is conceived shows a fresh sense of naturalism and exquisite decorative taste. This cast was executed through the courtesy of the Director of the National Museum of Naples, Italy.

97. ROMAN TORSO—CARRARRA MARBLE—I CENTURY—
W. 42.6 cm. (16¾")

This torso of a youth is said to have come to England during the XVIII century. Ex. Coll. Lord Melchette, who inherited it from his father, Dr. Mond. It has been widely copied.

98. ROMAN NEREID—BRONZE—I CENTURY B.C.—
H. 14.6 cm. (5¾")

This bronze was evidently an ornamental figure attached to a larger piece, as only the head is worked in the round. She wears an ungirdled peplos and holds the border of the apoptygma. A Roman bronze of excellent quality, inspired by a classical Greek model. Ex. Coll. Dr. Jacob Hirsch, New York.

99. ROMAN PAN—LEAD—I-II CENTURY—H. 17.7 cm. (7")

This casting of Pan, the god of flocks and shepherds and of all nature, is of lead. It is interesting to note that almost all Greek and Roman figures, including the bronzes, were cast solid. This was found in the Netherlands and dates from the Roman occupancy.

100. GALLO-ROMAN HEAD—STONE—III TO V CENTURY
—H. 44.3 cm. (17½")

Celtic art constitutes the most mature and original chapter in the evolution of art forms by the indigenous peoples of ancient west-central Europe and continues into the medieval period. By the beginning of the Chistian era the Celts (Roman Gauls) were no longer foraying barbarians. They were now settled throughout most of southwestern Europe and Romanized. This "severed head" from the area of Condate in the Rhone Valley follows conventions inherited from archaic Celtic traditions of the dead hero on the columnar core. It is conceived with hieratic immobility but withal realistic. Ex. Coll. H. M. Calmann, London. Purchased from the Bezalel National Museum of Jerusalem.

95

96

97

98

99

100

101. GALLO-ROMAN MOSAIC—COLORED MARBLE—III CENTURY—L. 302 cm. (118⅞"), W. 279 cm. (109⅞")

The power of the Rhone River at Avignon is so great that a bridge could not be built here in antiquity even by the Romans. Avignon was an important site of the Gallic Cavares and under the Romans a leading city of Gallia Narbonensis. Upon the breakup of the Empire, it was severely harassed by the barbarians and Saracens. This mosaic is from the ruins of a local Roman villa built during the latter half of the III century. The centerpiece depicts Diana and Callisto while scenes of the chase surround. It was brought to this country by the well-known dealer Joseph Brummer for William Randolph Hearst in May, 1926. It remained crated in the Hearst warehouse at San Simeon until 1962, when it was surreptitiously obtained by a Hearst employee for about 1/88 of the amount of money that Mr. Hearst had invested in it. Randolph Hearst, a son, telephoned me when he heard of this. I traced it and purchased it for about 14 times the amount the employee had paid for it, which still was a remarkable acquisition. Both a description and a photograph of this mosaic appear in "Inventaire des Mosaiques de la Gaule" published under the auspices of The Academy of Inscriptions and Belles-Lettres, Paris, Ernest Leroux, Editor, 1909. (See also detail shown as color plate, opposite page 41).

102. FOUR HISPANO-MORESQUE COLUMNS—WHITE MARBLE—XV CENTURY—H. (2) 295 cm. (116⅛"), (2) 272 cm. (107⅛")

At the conclusion of the text of Section I, we mentioned the rise of Islam and the spread of the Moslems, even into the European Spanish Peninsula. We showed examples of Moslem art in the lands of their origins. In the VIII century the Moors, chiefly of Berber-Arab stock, were converted to Islam and became fanatic Moslems. Originally the inhabitants of Mauritania (then much of northwest Africa) from whence they derive their name, they crossed to Gibraltar in 711 and overran the crumbling Visigoth kingdom, occupying Spain. They even traversed the Pyrenées into France but were turned back by Charles Martel in 732. But they remained in Spain, growing in wealth, splendor, and culture until their decline and eviction almost 800 years later. The contributions of the Moorish civilization to western Europe, and especially Spain, were well-nigh incalculable—in art and architecture, medicine and science, and learning. These columns were standing before Christopher Columbus sailed for America. They were in the courtyard of a castle in Navarre purchased by William Randolph Hearst through Arthur Byne and shipped to the Hearst Castle at San Simeon during June, 1935.

101

101 **Detail**

102

BRONZE DRAGON, HAN DYNASTY (CATALOG NO. 126)

SECTION III. THE ORIENT

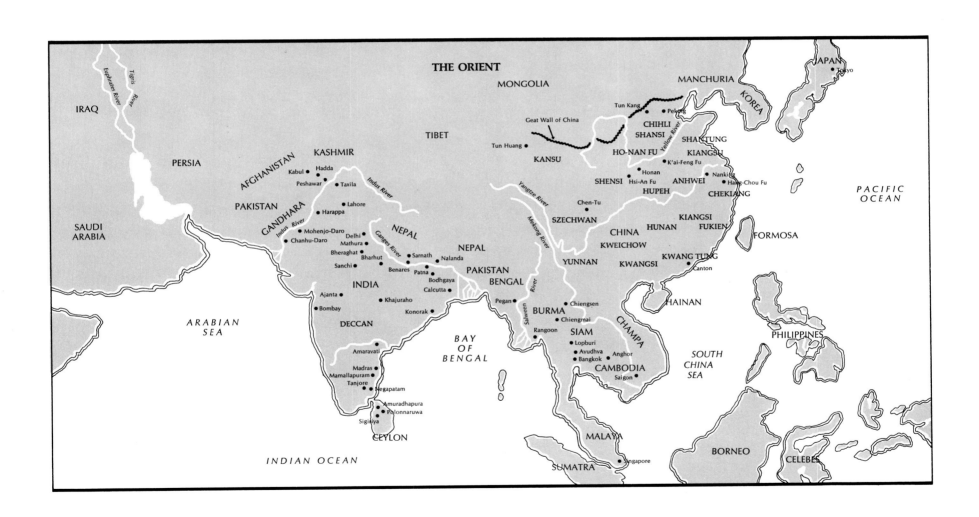

THE ORIENT

One need not be a Sinologist to "react," aesthetically, to a T'ang tomb figure or a Wei Buddha. These are accessible to our sensibilities if approached in the same mood of attentive passivity which we cultivate before more familiar western masterpieces. Oriental works may represent some alien divinities or symbols, but they are expressed according to certain principles of design and by means of a definite rhythm.

Indian art and the related Far Eastern arts are essentially hieratic, devoted to the personalities and acts of the deities and providing for their service. They were not produced with a view to aesthetic experience but as a means to edification. Few early secular sculptures are to be found. Chinese art does not as dominantly have this connotation, but here, too, it is sufficiently relevant to warrant a short explanation of the religious tenets which largely predicate it, some understanding of which will contribute to its appreciation.

Confucianism lays no claim to divine revelations. The Sage of China, Confucius (Kung Fu-tse, 557-479 B.C.), expressed "principles of right conduct and government" and his contributions were to ethical and social science. His teachings were hardly more than pure secularism. *Taoism*, developed slightly earlier, later corrupted, and then occluded, strives to attain man's compatibility with nature through mystical contemplation. It adopted many gods and later searched for the elixir of immortality. *Hinduism* is the western term for the religious beliefs and practices of most of the people of India today. Its Vedantic age did not develop a single fixed scriptural canon, but its ritualistic Veda Brahmanas, and philosophical Upanishads, and the great epics present an elaborate theological commentary. Hinduism is more than a religion. It is a complete way of life. Hinduism's triad of divinities are the remote deity who created the universe and who is equated with it, Brahma; Siva, the Destroyer; and Vishnu, the Preserver. Many cults with widely variant practices exist within Hinduism although orthodox Brahmanism holds the largest following. Initially based upon the ancient Vedic tradition, Hinduism has evolved into a most complex system of ritual and theosophy, regulating all human activities from personal moral qualities to sacrifices to the gods. Its tenet is of a universal soul to which all individual souls will be reunited after Maya, the illusion of time and space, is conquered.

Buddhism, one of the great religions of the world, is a system of philosophy and ethics founded by Buddha (Gautama Siddhartha, 563-483 B.C.). In origin closely related to Hindu Brahmanism, it had less formalism and a greater emphasis upon self-denial and compassion. In Buddhism the "noble eightfold path" leads through the end of desire to the final goal of escape from existence into blissful non-existence, called Nirvana. Buddhism was widely disseminated in India during the III century B.C. under the patronage of the pious Emperor Asoka and persisted for about a millennium. While it faded in India, the land of its birth, Hinayana Buddhism, its "purer form," survived in Ceylon and Burma. Mahayana Buddhism, with its huge pantheon of innumerable Buddhas and merciful Bodhisattvas offering universal salvation, entered China as late as the I century A.D. It spread to Japan principally through Korea. In Tibet, Buddhism became Lamaism. Another of the various sects which have arisen in Buddhism is Zen Buddhism, strong in China and Japan and now espoused by certain segments here. *Jainism*, which arose simultaneously with Buddhism, also as a protest against Hinduism, maintains the doctrine that everything in the universe, including matter, is eternal. It continues of minor importance.

The *Buddhist* art of *India* is more readily understood by the westerner than is *Hindu* art. In the *Buddhist* art, the salient impression is of linear rhythm. The contour is the most important feature of the form and is almost invariably of a flowing, continuous character. Its lovely equilibrium does not permit the elaboration of detail to destroy the general structure; whereas in much of the Hindu art we must abandon some of these demands and content ourselves with other qualities—diversity, multiplicity, and intricacy. But when one speaks of Buddhist India, always recollect that it was simultaneously Hindu India; that the so-called Buddhist and Hindu renaissance of the Gupta Period does not represent a reaction but rather the flowering and culmination of previous development.

Clearly ancestral to all later Indian cultures was the Indus Valley civilization of the third millennium B.C. with its urban centers at Mohenjo-daro and Harappa. The *original* inhabitants may have been Dravidians. In Section I we discussed the Indo-European dispersions, and we have followed the Indo-European migrations *westward* and *southward* down the Mesopotamian Valley. In Section VII we shall trace them through Europe. At the time of this dispersal, other Indo-Europeans trekked *eastward*. Ethnologists designate only this eastern branch as Aryan. At about 1800 B.C. these Aryan invaders coalesced their own culture with that of the lands they had conquered to form the Indo-Aryan civilization of the Vedic Period, which expressed itself in the sacred books, the Vedas, great poetic and philosophical literature written in Sanskrit, an Indo-European language. Aryans occupied the lands of the Indus River system and the Gangetic plain.

The intrusive Vedic Aryan people worshipped the great powers of nature by means of hymns and sacrifices, without the use of temples or images. The native Agamic-Dravidian people worshipped genii, dryads, tutelary deities, and a host of elaborate mythical cosmology. The ancient combination of these concepts forms the continuing traditional inspiration for all of the succeeding Indian art. The shape of man, gods, and all subsidiary figures are ordered in accordance with a living myth. They serve as symbols to carry out its rhythms. All very early Buddhist art shows no figure of the Buddha, only his symbols: his footprints, the wheel, the stupa, and the lotus.

Much later, western India suffered two further invasions. In 516 B.C., remember, the Persians under Darius occupied the Indus Valley. In 326 B.C. Alexander the Great controlled from Gandhara down to the sea. These contacts furnished the communications through which Persian and Hellenistic influences entered India during the following centuries. Gandhara became a great cultural area and should be so considered, instead of as a limited geographical locality. Alexander was the catalyst who caused the fusing of India's loose political units to form the first great Indian empire—the *Mauryan Empire* (325-184 B.C.). At the remains of the Emperor Asoka's great palace at Patna were found some of the earliest examples of Indian sculptural and architectural monuments in stone. The most perfectly preserved Buddhist monument to be seen in India, the great stupa at Sanchi, dates from the Mauryan Period. The relief illustrating Buddhist legends and scenes from the Buddha's ultimate incarnation are executed with a delicacy and wealth of detail suggestive of ivory celature.

The late Dr. Coomaraswamy considered, however, the first century and a half of the Christian era as the most critical period in the history of the art of India and the second to the fourth centuries that of the highest achievement. During the II century the many-headed and many-armed figures of Hindu deities appear for the first time. The prolific Greco-Buddhist school at Gandhara (II to V century) differs from the normal Indian type both iconographically and stylistically, but it exerted its influence widely in central Asia (No. 139) and to a lesser degree in China, Korea, and Japan. At one manifestation, due to Hellenistic influence, it flooded northern India with statues draped in the Greek manner and even produced a version of the Buddha himself with the features of Apollo—quite incompatible with his beatitudes (Nos. 142 and 145 a, b, c, d).

We cannot, here, go into the intimate, enchanting *Andhra* sculpture or the local schools of *Mathura* (No. 150) and *Sarnath* which initiated the later stereotyped face of the Buddha, set in eternal tranquility. The Gupta Dynasty (A.D. 320-600) temporarily unified India proper, and its art style was characteristically logical, sophisticated, gracious, and sensual. The famous cave paintings of Ajanta and Bagh belong to this time. Then followed the early, predominantly Hindu, Medieval Schools of *Harsha* at Nalanda; the *Pallavas* at Mamallapuram, where the rock carvings became the storehouse of South Indian form—the protagonist of the gigantic rock-cut myth. There were the *Calukyan* and the *Rashtrakuta* Dynasties. These are the people who developed the fabulous caves and for centuries, from the living rock, carved on the walls and ceilings, so that even today the beholder can relive the myths, surrounded by the lissome figures of nymphs and dryads. Would that we could, in this short compass, go into the architectonics of this period.

From about 850 onward the character of Indian art changed and hardened, no longer distinguished by plastic volume. Buddhism, in this land of its birth (No. 149), was finally abandoned for Hinduism. Now the tendency innate in all late art took over—greater intricacy and an overvaluation of technical skills as an end unto itself, although beautiful pieces were created (Nos. 137, 138). Medieval Hindu sculpture of the Deccan and Mysore, executed in a fine-grained dark chloritic schist, lends itself to an elaboration of detail (No. 141). Buddhist material of this period shows infinitely more restraint (No. 140). But by A.D. 1600, excepting in the Dravidian south, miniature painting had taken precedence over the other arts of India.

And so to *China*. The origins of the Chinese and their civilization are conjectural. Engaging hypotheses advance for them Sumerian, Egyptian, and other speculative derivations. There exists no records of ancient Chinese migrations. Probably their culture developed indigenously in the solitude of the "Middle Kingdom," cut off from all the world, and possibly they do stem from the legendary ancestor, P'an Ku. Their earliest chronicles go back to the second millennium B.C. when a Bronze Age culture, surprisingly developed, appeared in the basin of the Yellow River (Hwang-ho). The Chinese were already using the horse. Then, in the *Shang* (Nos. 106, 107) the *Chou* (No. 105), and the *Han* (No. 113), bronze ceremonial vessels, used in connection with nature and ancestor worship, materialized. These, for grandeur of form, dignity and ornamentation, and mastery of technique, have never been surpassed.

The *Shang* dynasty was brought to its end by the misdeeds of its last ruler. Condign punishment was inflicted upon him by the ruler of the principality of *Chou* who founded this dynasty. Nine centuries witnessed memorable development and territorial expansion. Chou art was pre-eminently symbolic and abstract (No. 120). We know that this was the period which produced the ethical and moral Chinese philosophical systems which persist until our own day. But the long Chou period ended in general anarchy.

From its known annals, China, like Greece, for all of its centuries, engaged in fratricidal warfare. China was continuously fragmented and emerged from a feudal chaos only to be split up into the "Contending States." Shih Huang Ti, inaugural builder of the Great Wall, in 246 B.C. founded his short-lived *Ch'in* Dynasty and federated China into a unified entity (No. 111). Upon his death insurrections again broke out, quelled with the ascendancy of the *Han* Dynasty.

Then, following internal consolidation, the nation experienced a halcyon period of expansion and foreign trade. The caravan routes to the west, to central Asia and even to the outposts of the Hellenistic world carried exotic trade goods. But during the middle of the *Han* period, at about A.D. 9, China indulged in the first of her state socialistic experiments—one now goes on. The results were disastrous. Then came price-fixing, government monopolies and even income tax. You recognize that venal political tinkerers, with no sense of double entry bookkeeping, have long harassed the productive elements of every populace. At any rate, after only about twenty years —calamity evidently moved faster then—of famine, ruin, and rebellion, the Han rulers re-established a normal economy, and prosperity followed. Literature and the arts revived. Sculpture in bronze contin-

ued, and stone now first made its appearance in quantity at this time. This was the time of the great Han mortuary vessels and the large, incised or pressed colored tiles and stone reliefs which decorated the interiors of tombs (No. 122). Clay figures of men, animals, houses, and utensils throw much light upon the life of the times (No. 108). The Han emperors welded China into the vision of a single empire, and to this day Chinese call themselves "the sons of Han."

As the imperial Han line grew weaker, rebellion and intrigue suffocated it. Followed four centuries of turmoil and constant wars. To domestic dissension was added foreign invasions by peoples from the north and west—Mongols, Hsiung Nu (Huns), and Turks. Ending Section II, we dwelt on repercussions in Europe from these events. Ephemeral states adopted Chinese culture, but they could not change it. As previously remarked, Buddhism reached China from India via the oasis route in about A.D. 65 and thoroughly infiltrated during the succeeding 400 years. Buddhist art reached a first climax during the late Six Dynasties (V-VI century). Monumental sculpture and steles were created, exemplified in the remarkable grottos of Shensi and Honan. Here the Buddha is depicted in an archaic, architectonic style, albeit with the passionless, spiritual calm and benevolence which is the essence of Buddhism, whereas the attendant figures achieved greater freedom and grace. Mundane backgrounds were first introduced. This was an era of assimilation and incubation, productive of many fine works (Nos. 110, 116).

Then, after this long period of political division, Chinese union was once more achieved in A.D. 618 under the *T'ang* Dynasty, and China became for this time the strongest and most magnificent empire on earth. Chinese arms were carried into Korea, Mongolia (No. 125), to northwest India, and into Tibet. To the T'ang court journeyed people of many lands and many faiths—Muslims, Nestorian Christians, followers of Manichaeism, and Japanese. Prosperity fertilized the arts. Buddhist, almost classical, sculpture, marked by slimness of figure and rhythmic grace of curve, often richly ornamented, attained a zenith; naturalism replaced conventionality, and the sculptured face, instead of reflecting a purely spiritual idea, approached humanization. The voluminous rotundity of the Buddha continued, however. Esoteric Buddhist sects offering the rewards of Paradise attracted wealthy donors. Many secular stone carvings were produced (Nos. 117, 123). To the T'ang period belongs Wu Tao-tsu, greatest of all the Chinese painters, whose style has exerted enormous influence on later times, not only in China but also in Japan. Pottery excelled in form (partly Sasanian Persian influenced), glaze, color, and texture. T'ang grave figures (No. 121) of great artistic merit, aimed at recognizable societal and individual portraiture. But again a period of chaos, and in A.D. 907 the enlightened regime of T'ang foundered as invasions and rebellions decimated the population.

The *Sung* Dynasty restored order to the country some fifty years later. Although it began auspiciously, during the course of its initial two prosperous centuries, it became pacifist and flaccid. Barbarian depredations further encroached upon the frontiers. Confucianism and Taoism gained practical ascendancy over Buddhism (Nos. 114, 115). Possibly this contributed to the retrogression of sculpture which now appears to be over-sophisticated (No. 118). Masterpieces of painting compensated, especially landscapes (No. 124). Painting from its beginnings in China had been considered a branch of calligraphy and was said to have had a divine origin. The Chinese are trained to use the brush from early childhood as it is their tool for writing, precisely as ours is the pen. Hence comes the masterful facility of absolute freedom displayed, relying mainly upon line and silhouette. The brush (*pi*) is used in ink or mineral colors on both paper (*chi*) and silk (*chuan*). The "Six Principles of Painting" had proscribed the techniques of the artist since the V century. Nevertheless, despite certain strictures, individual freedoms and techniques were brilliantly displayed.

At the inception of the XII century A.D., degenerating China lay drowsing in the rank scents of her then effete civilization, much as the Roman Empire had done on the eve of the barbarian invasions. Then came the forays of Genghis Khan's cannibalistic Tartar-Mongol hordes. China remained for a short time under the sway of the Mongol, Kublai Khan. During the ninety years of the *Mongol Yuans*, China—or Cathay as the Europeans called her—received western merchants, including the Venetian, Marco Polo. Christian missionaries briefly proselytized in China for the first time. Finally Mongol rule collapsed, and the purely Chinese *Ming* Dynasty inherited. The re-establishment of extensive foreign trade brought to China more Western cultural influences and art surrendered to embellishment. This trend has since prevailed.

But the miracle of China has always been its power to assimilate the invader and to conquer the conqueror. Her magnificent civilizations have bequeathed to us so many aesthetic triumphs. Herewith the Chronology.

SYNOPTIC CHRONOLOGY OF CHINESE DYNASTIES			
Ming Dynasty	1368-1642 A.D.	Han Dynasty	206 B.C.-220 A.D.
Sung Dynasty	960-1279 A.D.	Chou Dynasty	1122-256 B.C.
T'ang Dynasty	618-907 A.D	Shang and Yin Dynasty	1766-1122 B.C.
Six Dynasties	265-589 A.D.	Hsia Dynasty	2205-1766 B.C.
Three States (Wei, Shu Han, & Wu)	221-280 A.D.	Patriarchal Period	3000-2205 B.C.

Following are the principal periods in the art history of *Japan*.

SYNOPTIC CHRONOLOGY OF JAPANESE ART			
Edo Period	1615-1867	Heian Period	794-1185
Momoyama Period	1573-1615	Nara Period	645-794
Muromachi Period	1334-1573	Asuka Period	538-645
Kamakura Period	1185-1334	Pre-Buddhist Period	-A.D. 538

Comparatively isolated from other peoples during the Neolithic, *Japan* formed contacts with the mainland of China during her Bronze Age, which commenced over a thousand years after China's. Incredible, considering the proximity! Uniquely Japanese art, such as the Dotaku (bell-shaped bronzes) and Haniwa (terra cotta grave figures) (No. 131) are expressive of the ancient Japanese people. Japan has little stone suitable for carving. This led to the development of monumental wood carvings—sculpture was also created in beautiful, hollow, wood lacquer. Fired and unfired clay and the toreutic bronze art continued. The nation's ancient national faith was Shintoism, a simple system of reverence for ancestors, nature worship, and patriotic observance. The Japanese approached their art with incredible technical skill. It was a concrete material presentation in divergence with Chinese intellectual or symbolic traditionalism.

However, it was after the introduction of Buddhism in A.D. 552 that architecture, sculpture, painting, and the applied arts blossomed. Japanese communications with the Asian continent became increasingly intimate during the VII and VIII centuries. So the cycles of Japan's borrowings, absorbings, and returnings to native motifs started. The national adoption of Buddhism led to a golden age of Buddhist art, and we first find the cylindrical form and flowing drapes of the Kwannon (Chinese Quan-Yin) and the Miroku (Chinese Maitreya). At this time came the impact from T'ang China which saw Chinese models in painting and sculpture faithfully copied in Japan from the *Asuka* to the *Nara* periods. This dependence on China and her imports is well illustrated by the treasure of Emperor Shomu, which still exists in the Shosoin—a repository of lacquer objects, paintings on screens, bronze mirrors, textiles, enamel wares.

The early *Heian* Period still paralleled the Chinese in style. Japan even adopted the ideal of plump female beauty. However, relations between China and Japan deteriorated rapidly so that by the end of the IX century almost all intercourse between the two countries had ceased. At this time imperial control over Japan declined and it was replaced by the power of the nobles. The Japanese court was refined to the point of preciosity, and etiquette and euphuism overwhelmed morality. So in the late Heian or Fujiwara Period, bereft of China, there developed arts more purely and distinctively Japanese. Elegant opulence and refinement characterized this period (No. 130).

Civil wars led to the downfall of the then decadent Fujiwara rulers. Their successors established a new capital at *Kamakura* which gave its name to the period. The Japanese art style of the much earlier Nara Period was revived with the introduction of austere masculinity. The expression of this era is rendered in meticulous detail with the epitome of sculptural realism, albeit retaining a sensitive balance between the spiritual and the realistic (No. 134). Painting during this period continued in the *Yamato-e* style.

With the end of the Heian Period the Samurai (aristocratic warrior class) gained ascendancy over the nobles. The Samurai established military dictatorships, called Shogunates. The leaders of Japanese culture during this period were priests of Zen Buddhism. Because the Samurai found Zen attractive, the arts which had been associated in China with this Buddhist sect swept into the country. Sculpture, as in China under Zen, lost importance, and painting became reminiscent of the Chinese Sung masters (No. 132). However, art had this efflorescence during a turbulent political period. Sword furniture, the decorative ornamentation for sword guards, called *Tsubas*, produced during the *Muromachi* Period and onward, shows a technical mastery of the simultaneous use of gold, bronze, and iron (No. 136). Ironically, the sober enjoyment of the tea ceremony (*Cha-no-yu*) also originated at this time of turmoil.

Further continuing nation-wide social disturbances incurred by the warring nobles and traditional clans in the XVI century were finally suppressed by vigorous dictators. To forestall western domination the "closed door" policy was enforced in 1641, and Japan retreated into over two centuries of isolation. Art, which had been devoted to religion, came to serve the mundane interests of men's lives. Brilliant, ornate screen paintings, beautiful woodcut prints (No. 133), secular art (No. 135), costumes, and crafts flourished for the people.

The culmination of our Oriental dissertation is Indo-China, leaving Indonesia to the following Oceanic Section. *Cambodian* art before the VII century was directly influenced by the Indian tradition. In the Classic Period of the Khmer Empire (VII to XIII century) were evolved the pyramid plan and the great temple complexes of Angkor Wat, Angkor Thom, and Koh Ker, following an earlier development in Java (No. 148). Indo-China was so remote as to be scarcely touched by the main tides of history, and its wealth lay far from the main routes of the migrations. The powerful princes of Cambodia had grown rich from the production of perfumes and precious stones, of rice and spices. During the late XIII century the Thai (Siamese) commenced a series of revolts which eventually drove out the degenerative Khmer rulers, and their fabulous royal temple cities, abandoned, were overgrown by jungle (No. 152). Suzerainty passed from Cambodia to Siam. Following the fusion of the two cultures there was a rapid decline in the arts (Nos. 147, 151). Following are examples of the arts of the Orient.

CHINESE BRONZES

The origin of this type of accomplished bronze casting remains a great mystery. Its extreme sophistication and conventionalized design suggests a protracted period of incubation. Yet, there is scarcely a hint of these prior to 1700 B.C., when, at the site of the ancient city of Ch'angan, they appear full blown and at an apogee of technical accomplishment. One hypothesis is that an earlier Neolithic people were over-run by a bronze casting race who used the original inhabitants' clay or possibly leather vessels as prototypes.

These ritual vessels, the *Tsun*, the *Ku*, and the *Chueh*, were used for burial ceremonies and for harvest and fertility rites. In the Chinese concept of *Yang* and *Yin*, the *Tsun* and the *Ku* represented the two opposed forces which in their balanced opposition created the Universe and the energy of Life. The *Tsun* represented the Earth and the *Ku* the Heaven. The *Chueh* was the ritual food vessel and contained symbolic food. The design, engraving, and description of these vessels had great ritual significance.

105. CHINESE *TSUN*—BRONZE—EARLY (WESTERN) CHOU DYNASTY—1122-722 B.C.—H. 27.7 cm. (10⅞″)

This *Tsun*, with a superb emerald patina, has the *t'ao t'ieh*, pheasants, etc. in deep relief. Inscribed.

106. CHINESE *KU*—BRONZE—SHANG-YIN DYNASTY—1766-1122 B.C.—H. 29.6 cm. (11⅝″)

The *Ku* form almost invariably follows restricted lines, variations occurring only in the decoration which is always of delicacy and precision. In this fine example the curve of the profile may be compared to the echinus of a capital from the Parthenon, so sensitive is its springing sweep. In the ringed band toward the bottom of the piece are two cruciform incisions on opposite sides. The acanthus leaf-shaped upper portion shows the cicada (cricket), symbol of rebirth. Excellent patina. Inscribed.

107. CHINESE *CHUEH*—BRONZE—SHANG-YIN DYNASTY—1766-1122 B.C.—H. 18 cm. (7⅛″)

The *Chueh* was used for pouring hot libations. The tripod was for the purpose of standing the vessel in fire, and the two Chu posts were fitted into a handle to lift it when hot. Here is seen practically the entire gamut of bronze coloration. Inside the mouth, the lead-colored surface appears in original condition. Outside, many climatic changes have altered the color and composition of the bronze so that the surfaces freed from incrustation range from light straw green to deep brown. There are also rust-colored malachite and azurite deposits. Inscribed.

105

106

107

108. CHINESE HORSE HEAD—RED STONEWARE—HAN DYNASTY—206 B.C.-A.D. 220—H. 16.6 cm. (6½")

These heads were placed in the burials of nobles and officials. The plugs originally carried leather ears. Ex. Coll. J. L. Brotherton, San Francisco.

109. CHINESE HORSE HEAD—MARBLE—SUI OR EARLY T'ANG DYNASTY—LATE VI-EARLY VII CENTURY—H. 16.2 cm. (6⅜")

This is a particularly fine example and shows great movement. These heads in marble are extremely rare as most are of ceramic stoneware. Ex. Coll. Barling, London.

110. CHINESE HORSE HEAD—BLACK STONEWARE—SIX DYNASTIES—265-589—H. 14.4 cm. (5¾")

It is interesting to note the classicism of this head. It shows a conventionalization and a loss of virility during the time span between the Han and Wei Dynasties. (Note No. 108.) Ex. Coll. J. L. Brotherton, San Francisco.

111. CHINESE SWORD BLADE—BRONZE—CHIN DYNASTY—255-206 B.C.—L. 44.1 cm. (17⅜")

The blade has a deep sea-green patina, with a deeply engraved design on the hilt below the missing handle. (See photograph detail.)

112. CHINESE MIRROR—SILVER-BRONZE—T'ANG DYNASTY—618-907—D. 17.4 cm. (6⅞")

Mirrors, usually of bronze, were at times silvered as is this. Its ornate high relief includes fantastic animals and birds playing among grape tendrils, grapes, and interlacing foliage. This has the customary pierced central boss through which a ribbon or cord was looped as a handle. Mirrors were often presented to the emperor on his birthday by the courtiers. Mirrors were placed in graves not only for the toilet of the dead but also as a source of light. They were believed endowed with supernatural powers, guardians of marital fidelity, and certain magic mirrors were reputed to reflect a person's innermost thoughts.

113. CHINESE MIRROR—BRONZE—WESTERN HAN DYNASTY—206 B.C.-A.D. 9—D. 18.5 cm. (7¼")

These ancient mirrors are a specialty unto themselves. This rather large example is of a black bronze.

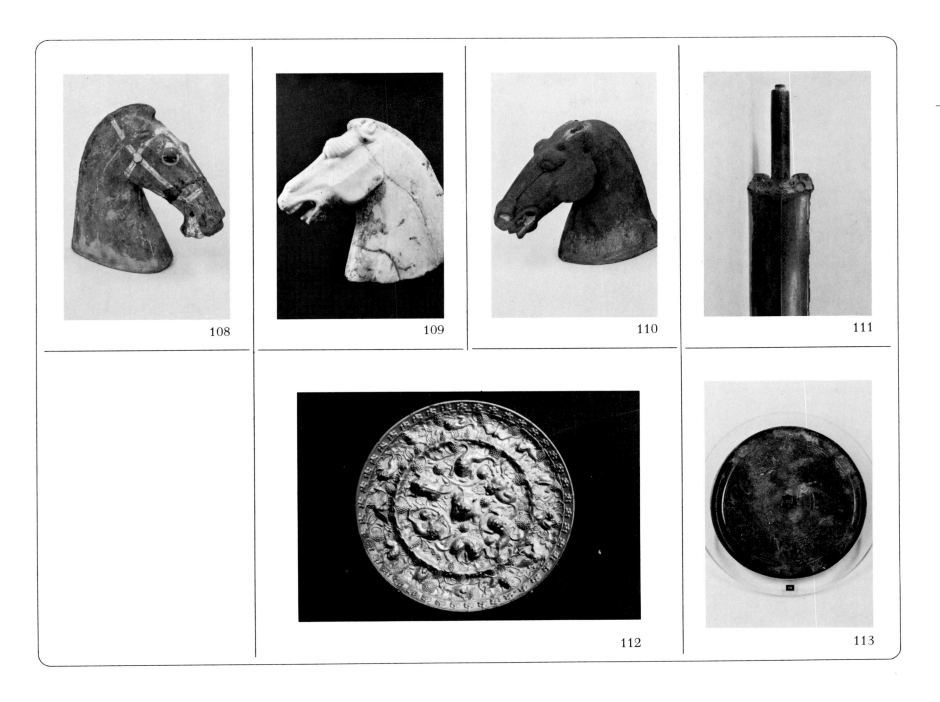

108

109

110

111

112

113

114-115. TWO CHINESE RELIEFS—BROWNISH MARBLE—
SUNG DYNASTY STYLE—960-1279—H. 48.2 cm. (19")

These two anaglyphs were part of a number which told the story of the founding, erecting, and work upon the great Temple of Po Quong, erected during the T'ang Dynasty (618-907 A.D.). The incised design is of celestial figures, and traces of paint show these were originally colored. It has been suggested that during the Sung Dynasty a great deal of restoration was done to enlarge this temple as part of it had fallen into decay. So these panels serve as rededication plaques to relate the great work that went on at this shrine which attracted many pilgrims. Following are free translations of the texts.

114. —————The temple and properties cover an area of 2600 acres. The temple has a staff of 300 monks and accommodations for 500 pilgrims.

115. The temple was founded on May 26 (year ?) T'ang Dynasty, by Emperor Di T'ang Ching Kun in the third year of his reign. The name of this temple is Po Quong. The name of the chief monk is Fa Gui Ken Sau.

116. MAITREYA BODHISATTVA—GREY LIMESTONE—
NORTHERN WEI DYNASTY STYLE—386-535—H. 31.7 cm. (12½")

This seated attendant Bodhisattva may have come from the caves of Lung Mên in Honan. The Maitreya Buddha, the Buddha of the Future, rules over the Tusita Paradise until the time when he is to return to earth again and preach the doctrine. Delicate but particularly fine, crisp carving.

114

115

116

117. CHINESE RELIEF—CONGLOMERATE STONE—T'ANG DYNASTY—618-907—H. 31.8 cm. (12½")

This relief, from Western China, represents a man playing a mandolin-like musical instrument.

118. CHINESE BODHISATTVA—LIMESTONE—SUNG DYNASTY—960-1279—H. 40.2 cm. (15⅞")

Here is presented the head of a Bodhisattva Buddha, carved over life size in the full round with hair dressed in a high chignon. It is Late Sung. Full cheeks, small mouth, elongated ears, stylized loti-form eyes.

119. CHINESE HORSE—UNGLAZED POTTERY—T'ANG DYNASTY—618-907—H. 35 cm. (13¾")

This spirited statue of a horse originally was covered by a transparent yellowish slip. It has a long saddle covering, roughened to suggest the texture of wool. Harness and straps are ornamented with palmette shaped plaques in applied relief. The saddle cloth shows blue paint, and there are remains of polychrome. There is a restoration of the left front hoof.

120. CHINESE MASK—BONE—WESTERN CHOU STYLE—1027-771 B.C.—W. 16.3 cm. (6⅜")

We purchased this *t'ao t'ieh* bone mask in Hong Kong from the collection of a member of the former Imperial (Ching Dynasty) family. It was authenticated by the expert Mr. Chen Jen-dao, who describes a somewhat similar mask in Archives of the Chinese Art Society XV, 1961, pp. 32, 33.

121. CHINESE HORSE AND RIDER—UNGLAZED POTTERY—T'ANG DYNASTY—618-907—H. 36.8 cm. (14½")

The decomposed slip over soft buff clay shows traces of white and colored paint. There is restoration on the head of the epicene rider.

117

118

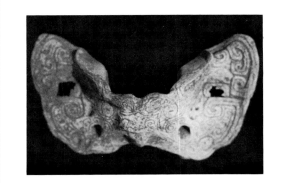

120

119

121

122. CHINESE TOMB TILE—GREY POTTERY AND POLY-CHROME—HAN DYNASTY—206 B.C.-A.D. 220—H. 1 m., 10.5 cm. (4⅛")

Hollow tiles, such as this, were used in the decoration of underground burial chambers. This example is stamped with registers of dragons, running rider, and floral, abstract, and geometric design. Ex. Coll. C. T. Loo, New York.

123. CHINESE LION—GREY WHITE MARBLE—T'ANG DYNASTY STYLE—618-907—L. 12.2 cm. (4⅞")

This figure of the couchant animal has a leonine head, with gaping jaws, heavy mane, and a single horn. Argillaceous matter adheres to the stone.

124. CHINESE PAINTING—INK AND LIGHT COLORS ON SILK —SUNG (SOUTHERN) DYNASTY STYLE—960-1279—H. 26.2 cm. (10⅜")

Taoism, through its love of solitude and contemplation, provided the Sung painters with many of their concepts of the appreciation of the beauties of nature. Comparatively few examples of this greatest period of Chinese painting are extant. This album leaf landscape is attributed to Fang K'uan. On the upper right hand corner it bears a Sung Dynasty official seal. On the lower left and right are two old collector's seals. Ex. Coll. C. C. Wang, New York.

125. CHINESE FRESCO—STUCCO WITH POLYCHROME—EARLY T'ANG DYNASTY—VII CENTURY—H. 31.5 cm. (12⅜")

In northern Mongolia between the VI and VIII centuries the very intricate cave temples of Kyzil were decorated with elaborate frescoes. Kyzil, during this period, was a thriving metropolis situated athwart the northern segment of the great trade route above the Gobi Desert between the Near East and China. This fragment of these frescoes depicts an Oriental female in Tocharian dress above a head of European type.

126. CHINESE DRAGON—BRONZE—HAN DYNASTY—206 B.C.-A.D. 220—L. 21.1 cm. (8¼")

This powerful form of the crouching dragon has a fabulous lustrous patination with extraordinarily large granulations. Ex. Coll. Chen Jen-dao, Hong Kong. (See color plate, this section.)

122

123

124

125

126

130. JAPANESE BISHAMONTEN—GILT BRONZE—HEIAN PE-
RIOD—782-1185—H. 18.1 cm. (7⅛″)

There are few XI century, Fujiwara Japanese bronzes extant.
Despite the fierce expression, armor, and lance of this Buddhist Guardian Deity, he is the equivalent of Kuvera, the Hindu god of riches and not be confused with war. The right arm
has been restored. In an excellent state of preservation.

131. JAPANESE HANIWA—TERRA COTTA—LATE TUMULUS
PERIOD—IV-V CENTURY—L. 28.1 cm. (11⅛″)

During archaic times, upon the death of an emperor, a ring
of his retainers, horses, animals, and birds was buried alive,
upright, around the slopes of his tomb to ward off malevolent
spirits. Here they suffered, died, and rotted. Later this custom
of immolation was abandoned and Haniwas (tomb sculptures)
replaced the living. There is latent vitality in this horse head
with its trappings. It is in the style of Kumagawa, Saitama.

132. JAPANESE SUIBOKU—INK ON PAPER—MUROMACHI
PERIOD—EARLY XVI CENTURY—H. 34.8 cm. (13¾″)

Suiboku, or black and white painting, is an ancient Oriental art
form. This was mounted as a *kakemono*—hanging scroll on bro-
cade. It is early Zen Buddhist by Sekkan and depicts a monk
riding an ox. Illustrated in T. Matsushita: *Suiboku Painting of
the Muromachi Period*, Tokyo, 1960, pl. 74, p. 72, text p. 21.

133. JAPANESE PRINT—MINERAL POLYCHROME ON PAPER
—EDO PERIOD—1857—H. 69.1 cm. (27¼″)

The master Hiroshige created this woodblock print titled Fuji-
kawa Gorge. It was one of a series executed in the artist's sixti-
eth year.

134. JAPANESE AVALOKITESVARA—LACQUERED WOOD,
GOLD LEAF, AND DECORATIVE JEWELRY—
KAMAKURA PERIOD—1186-1333—H. 74 cm. (29⅛″)

This sculpture and its lotus base have been largely cleaned of
600 years of accumulated incense smoke. Its surface and decorations are unrestored. It is very similar to the famous Kwannon (Chinese Quan-Yin) in the Tokyo National Museum. Cf.
Noritake Tsuda, *Handbook of Japanese Art*, fig. 188, p. 308.

135. JAPANESE EMA—POLYCHROME ON WOOD—EDO PERI-
OD—1603-1867—W. 25.2 cm. (9⅞″)

Upon this gay secular tablet is shown Monju—the future Buddha riding a tiger. Has beautiful lacquer box.

136. TWO JAPANESE TSUBAS—IRON WITH INLAY OF GOLD,
SILVER, AND COPPER—EDO PERIOD—1603-1867—H. 6.4
and 8.5 cm. (2½″ and 3⅜″)

Tsubas are sword guards, part of the decorative sword furniture representing masterpieces of metalwork. The workmanship on the reverse sides is extremely delicate. Inscribed.

130

131

132

133

134

135

136

137. NEPALI HEVAJRA AND SAKTI—COPPER GILT—LATE XIV-EARLY XV CENTURY—H. 23.2 cm. (9⅛″)

When obtained from the Nasli and Alice Heeramaneck Collection, this piece from Nepal was so encrusted that scarcely a trace of the gold leaf was visible. However, it has been grateful to the interminable cleanings of Leila Berg. Congratulations and thanks. It is a fantastically complicated casting of Hevajra with Sakti. It is jewelled with garnet and turquoise.

138. INDIAN GODDESS—WHITE MARBLE, VESTIGES OF COLOR—XIII CENTURY—H. 77.2 cm. (30⅜″)

From one of the renowned Jain sanctuaries of Mt. Abu in Rajputana. It is of the lotus-shaped type placed athwart the lower ring of the dome of these temples in semi-detached projection. Cf. Kramrisch, *Art of India*, pl. 135; Zimmer's *Art of Indian Asia*, Vol. 2, pl. 395.

139. AFGHANISTAN BUDDHA—STUCCO—IV-V CENTURY— H. 26 cm. (10¼″)

Greek classicism is evident in this head of the Buddha which still bears vestiges of polychrome. It is in the style of Hadda in Afghanistan.

140. INDIAN BUDDHA—SLATE—X CENTURY—H. 69.2 cm. (27¼″), W. 47.5 cm. (18¾″)

This presents the figure wearing a close-fitting, transparent, monastic gown which falls over the front part of the body in parallel string folds. It is in the three-quarters round and bears inscriptions, on the obverse and reverse sides, of the Buddhist creed and of its donor. From the area of Nalanda. Pala Dynasty.

141. INDIAN STELE—BLACK CHLORITE—CA. XI-XII CENTURY—H. 54.9 cm. (21⅝″), W. 25.6 cm. (10⅛″)

Siva and his wife Parvati, the Hindu divinities, are depicted with their various attributes. With three of his four hands he holds on either side the trident, and the three-headed cobra symbolizing his responsibilities and powers, and the citrus containing the seed of life; while his other hand embraces his wife, who in turn holds a mirror reflecting the perfection of the celestial world.

137

138

139

140

141

Its fabled mountain passes made the historic Gandhara region of West Pakistan a gateway to India, continuing through the valley of the Indus River. Gandhara was a province of the Persian Empire when Alexander the Great reached it in 327 B.C. Alexander's withdrawal quickly resulted in the founding of the Maurya Dynasty by Sandracottus, whose grandson Asoka, the most notable ruler of ancient India, for the first time in history brought nearly all of India, including Afghanistan, under one sway.

In the first century of the Christian era semi-nomadic Iranian tribes overran Gandhara. One of these tribes, the Kushans, became the leading political power in all of central Asia, and the region flourished until conquered by the Huns in the VI century A.D.

In the Gandhara area, two or three centuries after Alexander's incursion, a unique combination of Indian and Greco-Roman styles and features appeared in Buddhist sculpture. It must be remembered that the presence of Buddha in carvings such as at the Stupas of Bharhut and Sanchi was indicated by the symbols of the footprint, the wheel, the stupa, or the lotus. Since Buddha had entered Nirvana, which is beyond the visible world, mortals were not to behold Him, and He was not to appear as an *avatar*. But the Greeks and the Romans had long been accustomed to revealing their gods in human form. So it followed that here, too, the divine Buddha was also represented in anthropomorphic form, and He, rather than His doctrine, came to be worshipped. Gandhara developed a noted Greco-Roman school of sculpture consisting mainly of images of Buddha and reliefs representing scenes from Buddhist texts.

142. KUSHAN *YAKSHA*—ATLANTID—GREY SCHIST—II-IV CENTURY—H. 39.1 cm. (15⅜″)

Of the favored divinities of the pre-Aryan tradition still popular in early Buddhist monuments, were the yakshas, the tutelary deities of Indian family and business life. This bearded, winged Atlantid, a marine deity, is an obvious carryover from Greco-Roman mythology yet it is executed in an anti-classical style as to enhance the musculature of the figure. Illustrated and described in *The Connoisseur*, December, 1963. Cf. *Encyclopedia of World Art*, New York: McGraw Hill, Vol. VIII, pl. 411.

145a, b, c, d. GANDHARA CARVINGS—GREY SCHIST—II-III CENTURY—H. from 27.7 cm. (10⅞″)-40.4 cm. (15⅞″)

These reliefs, architectural temple decoration, show the classical Greco-Roman style adapted to Buddhism. Although belonging in the broad context of Indian culture, despite the religious inspiration, this may be regarded as an eastern offshoot of Greco-Roman art. But it could not have matured without the eclectic and syncretic tendencies of the Kushans. The iconography is most conservative. Rigid composition prevails, and there is a predilection for frontal representation and isolation of figures.

142

145a

145b

145c

145d

147. SIAMESE BUDDHA—BRONZE—XVI CENTURY—H. 25.1 cm. (9⅞″)

This beautifully formed head from Ayudhya, with configurations of marked ridges and smooth hollows, has predominantly linear elements. Plastic substantiality has been metamorphosed into sculptural drawing, not three dimensional mass suffused with inner life. Thus vitality yields to a sheer symbolization of transcendant ineffable spirituality.

148. CAMBODIAN BUDDHA—GREY-BROWN SANDSTONE—LATE MIDDLE KHMER PERIOD—XII-XIII CENTURY—H. 71 cm. (28″)

The ancient people of Cambodia were the Khmers of Sino-Tibetan origin. The ruins of the greatness of their kingdom are still to be seen in Angkor. Here is a Mucalinda Buddha, so called because the Buddha once sat for seven days in meditation under a huge tree beneath the roots of which dwelt the mighty serpent-king, Mucalinda. Against the natural cycle of the season an untimely thunderstorm arose. The Naga (snake) came forth and coiled around the body of the Buddha and, in the manner of an umbrella, guarded Him with his giant cobra hood expanded. And when the storm subsided, the Naga, Mucalinda, assumed the guise of a gentle youth and paid Him worship. Vestiges of original lacquer coating. Authenticated by Dr. Ananda K. Coomeraswamy, Alvin C. Eastman, and Dr. Alfred Salmony. Published: *Illustrated London News*, September 28, 1929. Ex. Coll. Quaritch-Wales, London.

149. INDIAN GANESHA—BLACK CHLORITE—PALA PERIOD —X CENTURY—H. 65.8 cm. (26⅜″)

In the pantheon of Hindu deities Ganesha is the God of Good Fortune. He is supplied with numerous arms to hold the symbols and the attributes of his power. He is here shown dancing on his *vahana* (vehicle), the rat, with garlanded *apsaras* above and musicians below. From Bihar.

150. INDIAN FRIEZE—BLACK CHLORITE—III-V CENTURY— L. 51.1 cm. (20⅛″)

This early stone carving is from Mathura, according to Dr. Chintamoni Kar, Keeper and Officer in Charge of the Calcutta Indian Museum, who was kind enough to review this section. The workmanship is excellent, but it is curious to note the retention of the motifs and technique that the earlier people had previously used for wood carving. Mathura works are more generally of red sandstone.

151. TWO SIAMESE BUDDHAS—BRONZE—XV CENTURY—H. 8.5 and 5.3 cm. (3⅜″ and 2⅛″)

It is estimated that the city of Ayudhya had a larger population than London in the XVI century. In 1767, captured by the Burmese and stripped of its treasures, it was burned to the ground. There are still miles of ruins to wander through. Innumerable deposits of these miniature "U Tong" images are to be found. Courtesy of M. C. Subhadradis Diskul, Chief Curator of the National Museum, Bangkok.

152. SIAMESE HAND—BRONZE—XIII CENTURY—L. 26.5 cm. (10⅜″)

This bronze hand was found at the old Mon city of Lopburi, Siam. It was probably part of a large Buddha. For our aesthetic reasons it is mounted horizontally and not in the original vertical position.

147

148

149

151

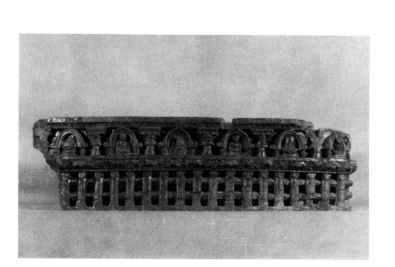

150

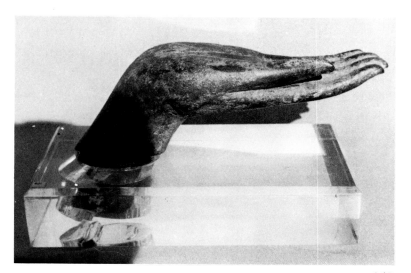

152

MELANESIAN MASK (CATALOG NO. 155)

SECTION IV. OCEANIA AND THE PACIFIC BASIN

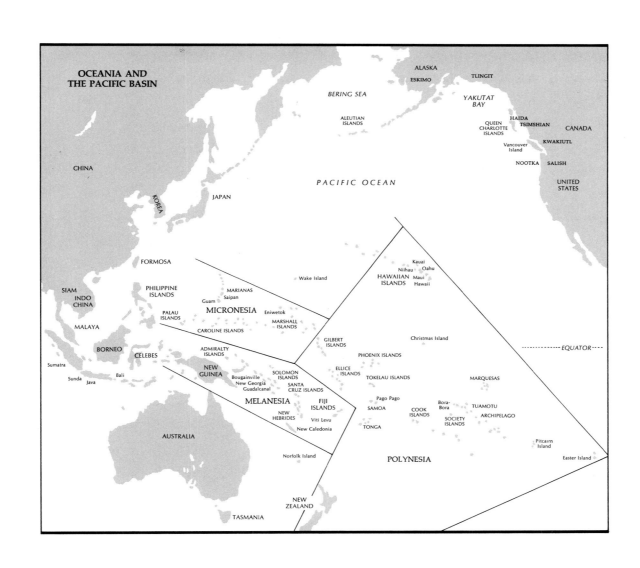

OCEANIA AND
THE PACIFIC BASIN

ALASKA
ESKIMO
TLINGIT

BERING SEA
YAKUTAT
BAY

ALEUTIAN
ISLANDS

HAIDA
QUEEN   TSIMSHIAN
CHARLOTTE   CANADA
ISLANDS

KWAKIUTL

Vancouver
Island

NOOTKA   SALISH

CHINA

PACIFIC OCEAN   UNITED
STATES

KOREA

JAPAN

FORMOSA

Kauai
Niihau   Oahu
HAWAIIAN Maui
ISLANDS   Hawaii

Wake Island

SIAM   MARIANAS
INDO   PHILIPPINE   Saipan
CHINA   ISLANDS   Guam

MICRONESIA   Eniwetok

PALAU
ISLANDS   MARSHALL
ISLANDS
MALAYA   CAROLINE ISLANDS

GILBERT   Christmas Island
ISLANDS

BORNEO   ADMIRALTY   EQUATOR
CELEBES   ISLANDS   PHOENIX ISLANDS

Sumatra   NEW   ELLICE
GUINEA   Bougainville SOLOMON ISLANDS   MARQUESAS
Sunda Java Bali   New Georgia ISLANDS   TOKELAU ISLANDS
Guadalcanal SANTA
CRUZ ISLANDS
MELANESIA   FIJI   Pago Pago   Bora-   TUAMOTU
ISLANDS   SAMOA   COOK Bora   ARCHIPELAGO
NEW   Viti Levu   ISLANDS SOCIETY
HEBRIDES   TONGA   ISLANDS
New Caledonia

AUSTRALIA   Pitcairn
Norfolk Island   Island
POLYNESIA   Easter Island

NEW
ZEALAND
TASMANIA

There exists overwhelming agreement among ethnologists that southeast Asia was the point of origin of the Pacific Oceanic people. Sunda Land was connected with the Asian mainland some 20,000 years ago during the Pleistocene, when, due to the melting of the Polar Ice Caps, the southwest Pacific rose as much as 300 feet and drowned the land bridges. Thus erstwhile landsmen became islanders, and the sea which surrounded them became an integral part of their ecology. They were of three diverse types. Contributing to the further hybridization of the island populations, there was a more or less continuous movement of Indonesians through the funnel of the Indies. However, the Negritoid component of their racial ancestry eventually predominated, and Papuan stock continues to this day. This archipelago, the source of the Oceanic people, is called *Indonesia*. While Australia is generally included in Oceania, we shall here confine ourselves to Melanesia, Micronesia, and Polynesia.

The remoteness of the far flung islands of *Micronesia* and *Polynesia* to the north and east presented formidable obstacles to the would-be emigrants from *Melanesia*. The tremendous distances were finally surmounted when these islands were entered by intrepid voyagers of predominantly Indonesian physical type, possibly from the Moluccas and New Guinea. While opinions differ as to the precise sequence leading to the discovery and settlement of Polynesia, few authorities any longer regard it as a migration launched in the Indies, but, rather, the immediate source of Polynesians is usually placed in central Micronesia, or eastern Melanesia, or a combination of both. Archaeologists have a difficult time with datings in all this area, as there are no stratified sites showing culture sequences. Grave goods, when discovered, do not differ markedly from artifacts of recent date. In general, chronological evidence is almost entirely lacking for the dolmens, stone statues, and menhirs of Melanesia; the conical pillars, buildings, and canals of Micronesia; and the ruins of megalithic structures—sacred places or *Marae* of the Polynesians.

Most of the islands of Polynesia were probably settled in the period beginning about 500 B.C. and continuing into 1000 A.D., a span of at least sixty generations. Polynesians in pre-European times were fairly homogeneous people in race, language, and culture, especially as compared with the more diversified Micronesians (Nos. 156, 158) and the extremely heterogeneous Melanesians (Nos. 153, 154, 155, 157, 159). The more robust physique of the Polynesians, anthro-

pologists believe, is simply the product of better living conditions after they left the poorer islands. Polynesians (Nos. 163, 164) left their imprint on many western Pacific communities and were a race with sea-faring tradition and a record of exploration, equalled in later times only by the Europeans.

In the sixteenth to eighteenth centuries, when the first white men explored the Pacific, their journals recorded elaborate native ceremonials and a kinship or organization that defied understanding because of its complexity. They reported little interest in the spiritual values of life, but revealed a consuming passion for genealogy, aristocratic hierarchies, and organized warfare. Today the clan, which is totemic, is the fundamental unit of the social structure. Hauntingly beautiful Polynesian song, dance, and feast are familiar to all of us.

Environment, as well as remote background, predicated material culture. Pottery could not be made in many islands without clay deposits. But there were gourds and coco shells. A simplistic form of wood carving evolved. Amongst the Maori of New Zealand these carvings, together with beautiful jades, excel (Nos. 160A, 162). The great stone heads and wood carvings of Easter Island find their stylistic relatives from New Zealand to the Marquesas (Nos. 160, 161). Highly conventionalized stone carving developed upon a tradition of wood carving, with variations, discernible from the Hawaiian Islands to New Zealand. This art style appears to have had its origins early in Indonesia (Nos. 165, 166, 167). The loom weaving and feather work are extremely recent. These people kept no written records, but transmitted their knowledge of things and events by oral tradition.

Oceanic art was the last of the primitive arts to be "discovered." The Cubists, searching for the basic geometric forms underlying the complex shapes of nature, first turned to African art. Then pre-Columbian material found its *aficionados*. But more recently the interest in the dream world and the subconscious, which first developed during the later phases of Expressionism, has contributed to our awareness of the magic art of Oceania. The affinity of this magic art with certain contemporary movements is not limited to concept and style, but can be observed also in the choice of material and technique. Is it possible the sterility which pervades this artificial western movement stems from the western artists' not sharing the prevalent belief of these Oceanic people that they are surrounded by ambulant spirits of their dead? Blue sea-world Oceania, raped initially, target of test atom bombs, clutched in the embrace of civilization! The basic trends in Oceanic Art may be summarized:

Melanesia: Natural forms exaggerated and distorted with rhythmic, organic, curved surfaces.

Micronesia: Natural forms simplified; ornamentation grows out of function and technique.

Polynesia: Natural forms geometrized; intricate surface patterns.

In the North Pacific, the *Eskimo* culture has evolved in a different manner from that of the American Indian and is quite similar to northeastern Siberia (Nos. 169, 171A, 172). The art of the Arctic, evolved in a harsh, white world, is one of primitive man's liveliest and most dynamic. It is imaginative characterization. It is surrealism. It is gay!

The *Indians* of the *Northwest Coast* and adjacent islands include the Tlingit, Haida (Nos. 168, 174), Tsimshian (No. 170), Kwakiutl, and Salish, all closely related. They have no religion beyond a belief in the existence of the spirits of the heavens, the woods, and underseas. The concepts are totemic. Here we shall remark on *Totemism*, as on this coast survives possibly the clearest manifestation of one of man's ubiquitous tenets. Totemism may be traced through all the ages and in all corners of the world. It appears in primitive material, on the shields of Greek heroes, the standards of the tribes of Israel: the ravening wolf for Benjamin, the lion's whelp for Judah; the five-clawed dragon of the Chinese, Montezuma's eagle. In medieval heraldry its symbols derive from the white horse of Westphalia, the bull heads of the Mecklenburgers, and other ancient armories. With the Northwest Indian, the clan's crest is a highly stylized animal and is combined with individually acquired crests. The resultant artifacts are often surprisingly sophisticated and frequently display a style tantalizingly similar to the arts of early Asia and the Pacific Islands, but little to other American Indians (Nos. 171, 173). Some examples of these cultures follow:

153. MELANESIAN HOOK—WOOD, POLYCHROME, AND COWRY SHELLS—XIX CENTURY—H. 61.6 cm. (24″)

These elaborately carved hooks were hung to keep belongings out of reach of the islands' prevalent swarms of rats and tree crabs. The mask is stylized and somewhat abstract, with an indigenous swordfish carved on the hook. From the Coastal Sepik River area of New Guinea.

154. MELANESIAN MASK—CARVED WOOD, PITH, SHELL— LATE XIX CENTURY—H. 49.5 cm. (19½″)

New Ireland in the Bismark Archipelago is the home of incredible, imaginative, technical virtuosity in carving and painted decoration. The eyes of this mask are univalve shells. Extremely rare. Cf. Jean Guiart, *Arts of the South Pacific*, trans. by Anthony Christie, New York: Golden Press, 1963, pl. 290. Acquired *in situ*.

155. MELANESIAN MASK—CARVED WOOD, SHELLS, TUSKS —EARLY XX CENTURY—H. 62.5 cm. (24⅝″)

From the ceremonial house (*tamberan*), Kanganaman, Sepik River, New Guinea, this wooden, carved mask is partially covered with painted limestone and insets of cowry shells and boar tusks. Human hair is attached. (See color plate, this section.)

156. FORMOSAN FETISH—WOOD—XIX CENTURY— H. 23.1 cm. (9⅛″)

This figure is Jukuban. Prior to the successive invasions of Formosa by the Portuguese, Spanish, Dutch, Chinese, and Japanese, two ethnologically different groups lived there. The Jukuban or "vanquished savages" now comprise about 500 tribes and have adopted Chinese modes and manners. The Saiban or "wild savages" still occupy the mountain fastnesses, and, although few in number, are still unsubdued.

157. MELANESIAN HEAD—WOOD, POLYCHROME— XIX CENTURY—H. 1 m., 31.8 cm. (51⅞″)

This monumental head is carved on both sides and is free standing. Ceremony rules art in New Guinea. None of these wood carvings survive long in New Guinea's tropical jungles, although it is known that stylistically they have been repeated for hundreds of years. Tadang Yamok.

158. MICRONESIAN STICK CHART—WOOD AND COWRY SHELLS—XVIII CENTURY—H. 61.3 cm. (24⅛″)

These stick charts, used for navigation in the Marshall Islands, are described in a book published in 1902, entitled *Die Stabkarter der Marshall Insulaner* by Albert Schück. *Die Stabkarten* contains many fascinating drawings describing the workings of these charts. Robert Louis Stevenson was very much interested in them. He formed the collection of these interesting forms now in the University Museum, Philadelphia. Cf. Carleton Coons, *The Story of Man*, New York: Knopf, 1956, p. 162.

159. MELANESIAN SHIELD—WOOD, POLYCHROME— XIX CENTURY—L. 191 cm. (75¼″)

From the Sepik River area, New Guinea, this carved shield shows a conventionalized naturalistic pattern.

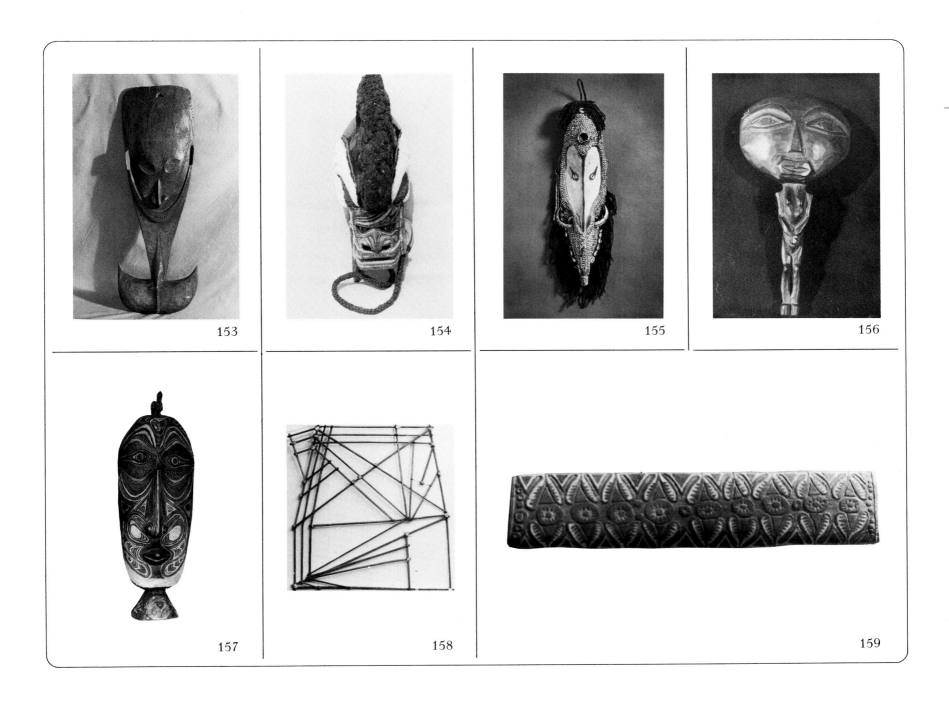

153

154

155

156

157

158

159

160. POLYNESIAN LINTEL—WOOD AND HALIOTIS SHELL INLAY—XIX CENTURY—L. 1 m., 17.3 cm. (43 3/16")

Government regulations now prohibit the export of these rare old Maori carvings. Ex. Coll. Hocken, N.Z.

160A. POLYNESIAN TIKI—NEPHRITE AND HALIOTIS SHELL —XVIII CENTURY—H. 10.9 cm. (4¼")

The *Hei-Tikis* of the Maoris of New Zealand were a traditional form of anthropomorphic figure in grotesque distortion, worn as jade pendants by women of high rank. Ex. Coll. Spencer-Churchill, England.

161. POLYNESIAN MOAI KAVAKAVA—TAROMIRO WOOD, BONE INLAY—XVIII CENTURY—H. 31.4 cm. (12⅜")

Easter Island is the home of the indecipherable petroglyphs and the monolithic stone heads weighing as much as eight tons. Emaciated figures such as this were carved in hard wood to venerate the spirits of ancestors. Note the accentuated rib cage. Eyes of obsidian, set in wing bone of bird. Ex. Coll. Miguel Covarrubias, Mexico.

162. POLYNESIAN MERE POUNAMOU—JADE—XVIII-XIX CENTURY—L. 33.3 cm. (13⅛")

The chiefs (*Ariki*) of the Maoris of New Zealand carried these "*meres*" as a symbol of rank. This is a particularly fine, translucent green jade example.

163. POLYNESIAN CLUB—WOOD, SHELL INLAY— XIX CENTURY—L. 45.4 cm. (17⅞")

This paddle-shaped club came from the Pago Pago area of Samoa. The design is geometric.

164. POLYNESIAN PADDLE—WOOD—XVIII-XIX CENTURY— L. 1 m., 21.2 cm. (47¹¹/₁₆")

The imbricated design of this ceremonial carving represents an incredible amount of intricate handcarving. It is from the Cook Islands.

165. INDONESIAN PRINTING BLOCK—ZINC AND WOOD— XIX CENTURY—L. 42.2 cm. (16⅝")

The great empires of Indonesia which emerged after the VII century were linked through the Buddhist and Hindu religions. However, Islam, introduced by Arab traders in the XIII century, eventually dominated. This block was used to print textiles and comes from Singaradja, Bali, through Java.

166. INDONESIAN STAFF—WOOD, COPPER, AND HUMAN HAIR—XIX CENTURY—H. 1m., 72.5 cm. (28½")

This type of wand was used by the Shaman of the Battak tribe of Sumatra for his magic. Legend alleges that the seat of its supernatural power is a paste, prepared from parts of the brain of a child sacrificed after he has promised that his spirit will obey the commands of the Shaman, sealed under the hair of the headdress.

167. INDONESIAN BELL—BRONZE—IX-XII CENTURY— H. 28.2 cm. (11⅛")

This Hindu-Javanese bell was sounded by means of a stick or mallet, not with a tongue. Its shape recalls that of a stupa, with the horizontal stripe round the middle of its body. The lion atop the bell is a usual theme.

160

160a

161

162

163

164

165

166

167

168. TWO HAIDA TOTEM POLES—ARGILLITE AND HALIOTIS SHELL—(a) XIX CENTURY, (b) CONTEMPORARY—H. (a) 58.4 cm. (23″), (b) 47.9 cm. (18⅞″)

Haida Indians of the Queen Charlotte Island area carve these totems or family crests of pale grey carbonaceous shale argillite. Soft and easily carved when dug, it then hardens. Women then hand rub them for days with sharkfin oil to produce their handsome black gloss. These Indians still carve their great wooden totem poles to a height of sixty feet and repaint them yearly. Here are the same forms, in miniature.

169. ESKIMO MASK—POROUS WHALEBONE—EARLY XIX CENTURY—H. 17.1 cm. (6¾″)

These masks, originally painted black and reddish brown, were made by the Eskimos in the vicinity of Point Hope, Alaska, north of Bering Straits. Cf. *Native Arts of Pacific Northwest*, Rasmussen Collection of the Portland Art Museum, Palo Alto: Stanford University Press, 1949.

170. TSIMSHIAN TOTEM POLE—BIRCH WOOD, POLYCHROME—XIX CENTURY—H. 85.7 cm. (33¾″)

Many totemic animals are carved on this smoothly rubbed, polychromed, miniature totem pole, including the raven, the eagle, the beaver, the frog, and the bear. See text for explanation of totemism.

171. SCRIMSHAW—WALRUS TUSK IVORY—XIX CENTURY—L. 72.5 cm. (28⅝″)

This tusk was probably carved by Alaskan Eskimos or American sailors. On one side is a decorated cribbage board and on the other a chart of the coast of the Seward Peninsula, covering only about 100 miles in either direction from Nome. This type of ivory carving is known as scrimshaw.

171A. ESKIMO CARVING—WALRUS TUSK IVORY—XIX CENTURY—L. 43.3 cm. (17″)

This carving is in the Okvik style from Little Diomede Island. Eskimos excel in the carving of ivories which combine the realistic and highly symbolic. Curiously, this ivory, which was considerably darkened and is now kept in direct sunlight, has bleached white.

172. ESKIMO CARVING—WALRUS TUSK IVORY—EARLY XIX CENTURY—L. 12.2 cm. (4⅞″)

Collected by the Danish anthropologist J. J. Warsaae in Eskimo Alaska, this sperm whale is beautifully modeled and has a warm patina. Perforated for attachment.

173. CHUMASH WHALE—STEATITE WITH SHELL INLAY—XVIII CENTURY—L. 13.1 cm. (5⅛″)

The Chumash Indians lived on the Channel Islands off the coast of California. They have left handsome, carved steatite pots and these whales. Smoke blown through the stem comes through the blow-hole.

174. HAIDA FIGURE—SHALE AND FISH BONE—XVIII CENTURY—H. 22.3 cm. (8¾″)

These figures were made for trade with the white man by the Haida Indians and are earlier than the totem poles. Their quality has established their niche in museum exhibitions.

168

169

170

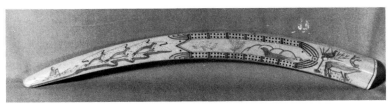

171

171a

172

173

174

DETAIL OF NAZCA FABRIC, SLIT TAPESTRY WEAVE (CATALOG NO. 246)

SECTION V. THE NEW WORLD BEFORE COLUMBUS

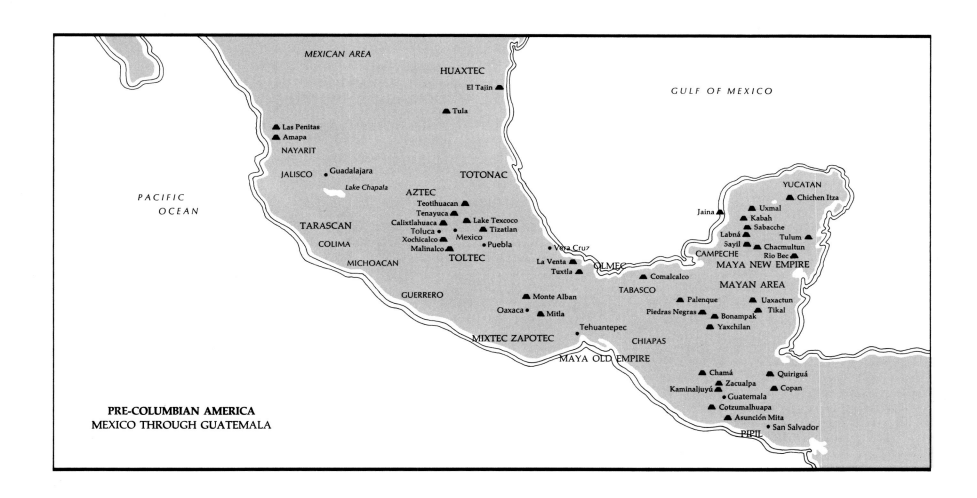

MEXICAN AREA

HUAXTEC

El Tajin ▲

GULF OF MEXICO

▲ Tula

▲ Las Penitas
▲ Amapa
NAYARIT

JALISCO • Guadalajara

TOTONAC

Lake Chapala

PACIFIC
OCEAN

AZTEC
Teotihuacan ▲
Tenayuca ▲
Calixtlahuaca ▲ ▲ Lake Texcoco
Toluca • ▲ Tizatlan
Xochicalco ▲ Mexico
Malinalco ▲ • Puebla
TOLTEC

TARASCAN

COLIMA

MICHOACAN

YUCATAN
• Chichen Itza

Jaina ▲ ▲ Uxmal
▲ Kabah
▲ Sabacche
Labná ▲ ▲ Tulum
Sayil ▲ ▲ Chacmultun
CAMPECHE Rio Bec ▲
MAYA NEW EMPIRE

• Vera Cruz

La Venta ▲
Tuxtla ▲
OLMEC

▲ Comalcalco

MAYAN AREA

TABASCO

▲ Palenque ▲ Uaxactun

GUERRERO

▲ Monte Alban
Oaxaca • ▲ Mitla

Piedras Negras ▲ ▲ Tikal
▲ Bonampak
▲ Yaxchilan

• Tehuantepec

MIXTEC ZAPOTEC

CHIAPAS

MAYA OLD EMPIRE

▲ Chamá ▲ Quiriguá
▲ Zacualpa
Kaminaljuyú ▲ ▲ Copan
• Guatemala

▲ Cotzumalhuapa
▲ Asunción Mita
• San Salvador

PIPIL

PRE-COLUMBIAN AMERICA
MEXICO THROUGH GUATEMALA

Man's initial appearance in the western hemisphere is estimated at a relatively late date, some thirty thousand years ago, and he is routed via the Bering Strait from Asia. We have noted the epicanthic eye fold, the sparse beard, and even the "blue spot," marks of the original Oriental still surviving on Mexican Indians. There were probably also small groups of other strains who arrived by crossing either ocean during late times, but numbers would be few and would soon lose their identity. The presence of fossil man in the Americas, on which there has been considerable controversy, is unproven. The progenitors of the men of Folsom, Cochise, and Sandia remain ghosts. Civilization, as we define it, had its beginnings after agriculture evolved, resulting in permanent settlements where man had both the time and the environment to think and act on collective social and religious problems.

NORTH AMERICA

In the previous Section we entered North America through the Alaskan Peninsula and, following the course of migrations, briefly mentioned the Eskimo and the Indians of the Pacific Northwest. Continuing south, our eclectic, but possibly myopic, eye finds the material achievements of the "noble red man" of the United States and southern Canada less impressive than those of the groups to the south. However, their cultures were admirably adapted to different simple types of life: that of the hunter, the fisher, the farmer of the plains and desert, and the forest dweller. Their archaic period ends more through definition than at a specific time. Actually the Woodland cultures represent a very small end product; Mississippi Temple Mound Cultures reached their zenith about A.D. 500-800, but this was essentially Mexican influenced; the Plains Indians were primarily nomads dependent upon the migrations of the bison; and in the southwest—the locus of the Hohokam and Pueblo cultures, where the highest level was reached and the "apartment houses" built—the dismal years of drought and enemies between 1273 and 1299 precluded further development. (See, however, Nos. 174a and 174b.) So, let us examine their neighbors to the south. This immensity we divide into two areas—"Mexico through Guatemala" and "Middle America through the Andean Area." Pre-Columbian gold and jade are treated separately, beginning on page 142.

MEXICO THROUGH GUATEMALA

The indigenous, magnificent achievements of the *Pre-Columbian* peoples of this area may best be appreciated by a visit to some of the sites, which are now comparatively easily accessible. Only through the combined impact of architecture, sculpture, pottery, and wall decoration can we comprehend the aesthetic accomplishments of these early Americans. Their remote history remains a bit of an enigma as fact and fiction are inextricably interwoven, and archaeology is confronted with an aura of myth, legends, and poetry which emanates from ruin, writing, and archaeological exploration. Maize was their food staple from primordial time.

Formative sites reveal decorated pottery, well-worked implements, and small modeled terra cotta figurines, predominantly female, which probably were connected with fecundity rites. Much of this has a similarity to other archaic and pre-dynastic cultures of the world. The potter's wheel was not employed. Although the wheel has been found on children's toy carts, it was not utilized for draft. However, great strides are evident during the latter part of this period, as, by the beginning of the Christian era, these people possessed all of the ingredients necessary for the mature civilization which flowered during the following Classic Epoch.

Before A.D. 200 the great ceremonial center of *Teotihuacan*, with its famous pyramid temples, was built a short distance northeast of present Mexico City by a people about whom practically nothing is known. This area will logically serve as our focal point for orientation as we discuss pre-Columbian Mexico. From here goods and ideas were traded with the *Zapotec* nation. Their capital city was built with great complexity and grandeur at Monte Alban, near present Oaxaca (Nos. 209, 213, 214). Here the Zapotecs enjoyed a truly valid early civilization formed centuries before the Christian era. They sculpted an entire mountain and its outlying spurs as a home for their gods. The highest crest was leveled off and laid out as a central plaza a thousand feet long and 650 feet wide. From the flanks of this stone mountain they hewed roads, terraces, and courts until the sacred area stretched for many miles. Then on this dramatic site, they built their pyramids, their temples, their celestial observatory, and their religious ball courts. The surrounding hills were covered with smaller structures, temples, and tombs. These were the people who carved the tantalizing undeciphered glyphs on the Dancer stones. These "danzantes" (No. 209)—so called because of their dancer-like postures—are low reliefs of life-size figures of naked men. The faces of these antic creatures vary from tiger cubs to distinctly Negroid humans, to old, bearded men with Semitic features. Their significance is unknown. Dr. Alfonso Caso, the excavator and interpreter of Monte Alban, made his richest find in Tomb 7 when he discovered the treasure of gold, jade, crystal, and turquoise now in the Oaxaca Museum. But this treasure was of the later *Mixtec* era. Both the Zapotecs and Mixtecs were consummate goldsmiths. Zapotec tombs are the most elaborate in the Americas. Around 900 Monte Alban declined. Mitla, with its "perfect" temple became the seat of the high priests. Then the Mixtecs superseded the Zapotecs and effected their cultural renaissance with a genius in ceramics and the working of gold (Nos. 208, 210, 212). Under Aztec suzerainty, the Mixtecs prevailed in this area until the conquest.

In contrast to our knowledge of the Zapotecs, even the language of the people of *Teotihuacan*—who built the Sun Pyramid in ground area vast as the largest Egyptian pyramid of Cheops, the Moon Pyramid, the Street of the Dead, and the fifteen satellite pyramids—is unknown. We can only admire magnificent sculpture, carved in stone, which includes heads of serpents and other grotesque portrayals supposedly representing Tlaloc, the rain god. Fine frescoes are still visible here. Teotihuacan material has been found as far south as the Maya cities of Guatemala and at Copan in Honduras. So there was extended trade. Obviously there was a large population. Probably their saga will never be known. We surmise that their Classic Period, which is reckoned from the II to the VIII centuries and is approximately coincidental with the Maya Classic, was a long span of comparatively peaceful development. Aside from a few painted battle scenes, there is a marked absence of warriors and strife (No. 179).

Archaeological evidence supports the theory that the *Toltecs* built up pressures in the lands north of Teotihuacan. They destroyed it at about 856 in a huge conflagration. Then they erected their cultural metropolis, Tollan, near modern Tula, for their priest-king, Quetzalcoatl (No. 175). "Quetzal" is a species of bird; "coatl" means snake. This personage has caused tremendous confusion among historians and archaeologists. For the Teotihuacan civilization, Quetzalcoatl was a god; for the Maya and Toltecs, he was a priest-king; in Yucatan he was known by the name of Kukulcan; and during the Aztec Period, Quetzalcoatl became a title. From Tula, the Toltecs migrated south through Mesoamerica using military might and new gods. At about A.D. 900 they finally occupied the Maya city of Chichen Itza in Yucatan and then rebuilt it with a distinctive Tula flavor. This general movement of the Nahua-speaking tribes ushered in the Post Classic Period with a strong emphasis on warrior cults and human sacrifices to their powerful gods (No. 176).

The *Maya* were the intellectuals of the New World. They were the Greeks of Middle America just as the Aztecs may be likened to the Romans. Their area extended from Yucatan, Northern Guatemala, and adjacent Mexico through the Isthmus of Tehuantepec and southeast into Honduras and Salvador. They had a knowledge of astronomy and an amazingly accurate calendar, transcending that of then contemporary Europe's Julian Calendar. They had evolved chirography. They even had a sign for zero—the crowning development of the numerical system which appeared in Europe only after the X century with the adoption of the Arabic system. The scale of their architecture was colossal and their carved stone decoration absolutely magnificent (Nos. 215, 218). The corbeled arch was employed. Copper and gold were fabricated, using many techniques. The pottery and ceramics of the Maya were probably the finest in the Americas (Nos. 217, 219). However, the only domesticated beast of burden in the Americas before the introduction of the horse by the Spaniards was the llama of South America.

The Maya horticultural peasant class was ruled by a theocracy. Until today, the natives of this region bear a startling resemblance to the Maya pictured in their ancient art (Nos. 216, 220). They resemble amazingly the early Anatolian Hittites. The rustic Yucatecan today still generally speaks, not Spanish, but the old Maya language. After the Toltecs invaded this country, a Toltec-Maya civilization arose. However, by this time the original Maya civilization was already regressive. Population had greatly declined, and huge cities, laboriously created over the previous centuries, had been inexplicably abandoned. This is generally ascribed to protracted soil exhaustion; possibly the cause was epidemics or earlier raiders. Probably this answer could have been supplied us by the codices, the ancient Maya manuscripts burned by the conquistador fanatic, Spanish

CHRONOLOGY—MEXICO THROUGH GUATEMALA

			Northern & Western Mexico	Central Mexico	Oaxaca & Puebla	Central Veracruz	Southern Veracruz & Tabasco Olmec Area	THE MAYA AREA Yucatan Peninsula	Lowland Guatemala, British Honduras	Highland Guatemala	Honduras, El Salvador
SPANISH CONQUEST		1520 A.D.									
POST-CLASSIC PERIOD	Late	1200 A.D.	*Seri* Casas Grandes | *Tarascan* Tzintzuntzan Pátzcuaro	*Aztec* Tenochtitlán	*Mixtec* Monte Albán V	Cempoala		*Mayapan*			
POST-CLASSIC PERIOD	Early	900 A.D.		*Toltec* Tula	*Zapotec* Monte Albán IV — Cholula			*Toltec* Chichén-Itzá	Area Largely Abandoned		Suchitoto
CLASSIC PERIOD	Late	600 A.D.	Nayarit Jalisco Colima	Teotihuacán IV	Monte Albán III	Tajín III | Remojadas III		*Puuc Florescent* Uxmal Jaina	*Tepeu* Quiriguá Palenque Yalloch Uaxactún	*Pamplona-amatle* Lake Amatitlán	Ulua Valley Yojoa Copán San Salvador
CLASSIC PERIOD	Early	300 A.D.		Teotihuacán III Teotihuacán II		Tajín II | Remojadas II ; Tajín I | El Faisan	Upper Tres Zapotes	Regional Styles	*Tzakol* Uaxactún Tikal	*Esperanza* Kaminaljuyú	
PRE-CLASSIC PERIOD	Late	500 B.C.	Guerrero "Mezcala Style"	Teotihuacán I Ticomán	Monte Albán II	Remojadas I	Middle Tres Zapotes	La Venta	*Chicanel* Uaxactún	*Arenal* Kaminaljuyú	
PRE-CLASSIC PERIOD	Middle	1000 B.C.	Chupícuaro | Apatzingán	Tlatilco	Monte Albán I		Lower Tres Zapotes		*Mamon*	*Miraflores* Kaminaljuyú	Playa De Los Muertos
PRE-CLASSIC PERIOD	Early	1500 B.C.		Zacatenco						*Las Charcas*	

108

(Chronology courtesy Heye Foundation)

Bishop Landa. All religious, medical, and mathematical treatises went up in flame and smoke when the Spaniards decided to exorcise the heathen devil. Today, although the Maya numerical system is easily understood, our experts grope in the dark for the decipherment of Maya script. Some of the first Spanish ecclesiastics learned to read and write in this script, but the art has been lost, and the only three codices extant, all in European museums, are mainly a compilation of dates, presenting historians with more problems than information.

Other seemingly disparate cultures were the mysterious early *Olmecs* of Tabasco and southern Vera Cruz—the La Venta area, responsible for the carved stone "Colossal Heads," infantile faces, and unusually beautiful jades. But archaeology has not exactly placed them in the time scale (Nos. 193, 194). North of the Olmecs in Vera Cruz are found the distinctive carved stone "Yokes" (No. 188), "Palmates" (No. 189), and "Hachas" (Nos. 182, 184), and the mold-made figurines with curious smiling faces (Nos. 191, 192) of the *Totonacs*. These are the well-known *caritas sonrientes* (smiling faces). Does the smile represent the ecstasy of some dance, or are they prepared, sacrificial victims with faces contorted by drugs? No other section attained such perfection in stone working (Nos. 183, 186, 187). Their pottery is often uniquely decorated with bitumen (Nos. 185, 190).

West and north of the Valley of Mexico a large area extending to the Pacific coast had been isolated by the Sierra Madre Mountain Range. At about A.D. 500 ripples of Classic activity penetrated here, and there was an awakening from a formative stage of expression. *Tarascan* is the generic name given the culture as a catchall, despite the dissent of some archaeologists of this region, which embraces the present states of Colima (Nos. 195, 197), Jalisco (No. 200), Nayarit (No. 201), Michoacan (No. 198), and Guanajuato. The Tarascans in this forested region of western Mexico represent a very individual culture which neither the ancient aggressive military people nor even the Spaniards succeeded entirely in subduing. Even today people venture into the remote mountain fastnesses of the Huicholes with military escorts. Sections close of the north-south route of migration and conquest reflect Tula-Toltec influences (Nos. 202, 205). Further west in Colima and Nayarit, the sculptor, unrestricted by

religious demands, was creating highly distinctive images in clay— *barro* (Nos. 196, 203). These depict people in every attitude of daily and ceremonial life, including fascinating models of houses with their occupants, funeral scenes, sex scenes, dance groups, ceremonial games, and battle scenes. Animal figures, especially the dogs of Colima, are realistically charming (No. 206). The pottery shows a high sense of humor (No. 204). Many of the austere figures are of the horror school, but here, too, is found fine authentic sculpture (Nos. 200, 207).

Again in history the new barbarian arrives. In the XII century, the fiercely militant *Aztecs*, a conglomerate of tribes, descended from the north into the Valley of Mexico. Forthwith, they dominated this entire area, and a composite civilization, based on a Toltec and a Mixtec-Puebla heritage, was forged, with its capital at Tenochtitlan where modern Mexico City now rises.

The Aztecs exacted from their neighbors tributes of goods and, more importantly, captives to sacrifice to their gods. They maintained protected trade routes that reached Costa Rica and Panama. Great activity in arts and crafts filled colorful market places with displays of textiles, pottery, featherwork, jewelry, idols, and ceremonial paraphernalia of clay and stone, flowers, and produce. Temples and intricate sculpture took on an air of austere brutality (No. 177). Through central, eastern, and southern Mexico, the stress was now on the emotional overtone of form, rather than objective representation (No. 181). The artist distorted and eliminated to achieve his desired effect (Nos. 178, 180).

Then came the *Conquest*. All the world knows of the exploits of Hernando Cortéz, starting in 1518. The incredible courage, the cruelties, the treacheries and bigotry of the intrepid Conquistadores are well chronicled by Bernal Diaz del Castillo. The Conquest, however, put an end to all traditional art production, which was for the most part connected with religious practice. The Catholic Church of Spain issued an edict abolishing native ritual. This order was so enthusiastically carried out that most of what we consider art was destroyed in both Americas. The white man's lust for gold completed the pillage. It is ironic that the finally dominant people, the Aztecs, with their great civilization and bloody religion, came from oblivion into full flower for only a few hundred years and then were obliterated by the Conquest. So, these civilizations lay dead in the minds of men until late in the XIX century. Archaeological and ethnological research has since been most rewarding.

It is imperative that we pursue the great accomplishments of these aborigines. As early as the first century after Christ, their art was already condensed and mature. From its architecture to its jade carvings, it speaks a language highly articulate, rich, although often flamboyant, and compares favorably with the high arts of the continents. We have seen the incredibly beautiful wall paintings, including those of Bonampak. The classic ball courts had a religious function. Visualize the wondrous sight of the ceremonial centers in pristine splendor at the time of the rituals. Even today sufficient remains to show that no one center exhibited all of the strongest qualities of each architectural or embellishment medium, the bold carving of one being matched by the sensitive fresco or relief work of another. Although great civilizations rose and fell during this thousand-year period, it was one of constant cultural development and tremendously vital artistic activity. Each culture had its particular individual characteristics with continuing variations. This virility and endless innovation holds us. An impeccable sense of design couples with a great feeling of dignity.

Pre-Columbian pyramids were entirely different in concept from the tomb-pyramids of Egypt. They were somewhat similar to the smaller ziggurats of Mesopotamia and were certainly independently invented. Very few contain passageways or chambers. They were generally huge, truncated mounds of earth which served as a platform for an altar or temple so that thousands of worshippers could view the ceremonies and sacrifices from the large-floored plazas below. They were ordinarily faced with stucco, or dressed and carved stone, and elaborately colored and decorated. There obviously was great social organization, as tremendous numbers of people were necessary for this scale of building. Our late friend, Professor George Brainerd, calculated that predicated upon mass, the earth moving alone, without ornamentation, would have required a working force of 6,000 men for five years at the Pyramid of the Sun in Teotihuacan.

These people had no gunpowder, but they performed an awesome job of slaughter. They had a predilection for ritual cannibalism. The objective in warfare was not to kill the enemy, but to capture him alive for later sacrifice to the insatiable gods. It is recorded that on one holiday three thousand human sacrifices were made. High up on the pyramid's altar the victims were stretched upon the block for immolation. From their living bodies their beating hearts were plucked and offered to the deities of sun, earth, and rain. Then the corpses were tumbled all the way down the pyramid steps where the waiting multitude butchered them to be boiled and eaten—history's most gruesome abattoir. In Europe, though, ritualistic cannibalism was practiced in Sicily as late as the 1860's.

That contemporaneous Franciscan friar, Father Bernardino de Sahagun, realized that an understanding of the lore, the legends, and the normal life of these people was essential for their conversion to Christianity. Years were spent as de Sahagun and his native pupils laboriously compiled a tremendous historical work. A perusal of this first-hand account brings us close to the intimacies of the vanished empires of the Toltecs and the Aztecs. "Civilized" man made a trade with these people, who initially received him in a trustful, frequently generous fashion. Christianity gave smallpox, alcohol, the genocide of Cortéz and Pizarro and their followers, and the Indian reservation, and "civilization" received lands, gold and silver, potatoes, chocolate, tobacco, peanuts, pineapples, tomatoes, corn, cocaine, and quinine. What a Point Four program!

Examples of the artifacts of these cultures follow.

174a. AMERINDIAN PETROGLYPH—STONE—ARIZONA—
XIII-XIV CENTURIES—H. 92.3 cm. (36⅜″)

Petroglyphs are found on cliffs and boulders throughout the southwestern United States. Archaeologists are uncertain as to their exact meaning.

174b. ZUNI CEREMONIAL JAR—ARIZONA—LATE
XIX CENTURY—D. 30.5 cm. (12″)

This handsome vessel is typical of the high degree of craftsmanship attained by the Indians of the southwest United States. Used in the ritual of the *kiva*. The "heartline" deer design, common to many cultures, persists even today.

174a

174b

175. TOLTEC PETROGLYPH—LIMESTONE—TAMIULAPAC—
CA. 900—H. 45.6 cm. (18")

This relief was part of a wall decoration from a temple near Tula. It portrays a jaguar with a human heart suspended from a cord around its neck. The major portion of the material in this book is the result of our own peregrinations. However, our thanks to the late Earl Stendahl for our acquisition of many fine pieces, including this petroglyph.

176. TOLTEC JAGUAR—STONE—GUERRERO—CA. 800—
L. 74.7 cm. (29½")

This powerful jaguar head is cut as a stone tenon and was mounted as a projection from the facade of a building. It exemplifies the Toltec style.

177. AZTEC SNAKE—PORPHYRY—VALLEY OF MEXICO—
CA. 1400—H. 25.8 cm. (10⅛")

The feathered serpent was first a Toltec god-king, whose worship spread over a large area of the New World as Quetzalcoatl. The rattlesnake is woven into the knot typical of the reptile. Teeth and tongue are conventionalized in the best Aztec tradition, and the scaly rattle feathers, conscientiously portrayed, have been used with good decorative sense against the smooth coils.

178. AZTEC XIUHTECUHTLI—STONE—VALLEY OF
MEXICO—CA. 1400—H. 42.3 cm. (16⅝")

Xiuhtecuhtli, Lord of Fire, is always depicted as a decrepit, almost toothless, old man (Huehueteotl). He sits with bowed head, supporting a huge bowl in which incense was burned.

Such a divinity peculiarly fits a volcanic country, and his age suggests the manifest antiquity of mountains. George Vaillant traces him back to the Teotihuacan civilization and considers that his continuous worship would make him the oldest god ritualistically shown in Middle America even though the Mother Goddess of Corn and Growth may represent an earlier concept. Ex. Coll. Guillermo Echaniz, Mexico City.

179. TEOTIHUACAN JAR—FRESCO WARE—VALLEY OF
MEXICO—CA. 700—H. 13.5 cm. (5⅜")

This cylindrical jar was found at Teotihuacan. The tripod legs have an openwork design. The motif is of the tree-mountain symbol and the year sign. The painting is fragile fresco on brown ware.

180. AZTEC HEAD—TUFFA STONE—VALLEY OF MEXICO
—CA. 1400—H. 20.6 cm. (8⅛")

This head portrays Ehecatl, the Aztec god who directed the good winds and helped agriculture by blowing the pollen to germinate life.

181. AZTEC CIUAPIPILTIN—ANDESITIC ROCK—VALLEY
OF MEXICO—CA. 1200—H. 41.3 cm. (16¼")

This represents the woman who died in childbirth and became a deity. Each day the Aztec sun was carried in a litter to its zenith by the souls of warriors slain in battle or upon the sacrificial stone. Then the Ciuapipiltin conducted the sun to its setting. Published: Southwest Museum's *Master Key*, January 1961.

175

176

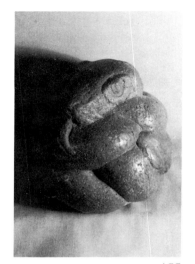

177

178

179

180

181

182. TOTONAC HACHA—ANDESITE—VERA CRUZ—
CA. 700—H. 35.6 cm. (14″)

A distinctive Totonac type of stone carving, the use of which is
unsettled, is found in the ax-shaped pieces called *hachas*, which
is merely the Spanish word for ax. They have also been found
in the highlands of Guatemala. This *hacha*, of the Late Classic
Period, has an unusually complicated design of a complete
anthropomorphic figure with a feline head, surmounting the
human profile. Both sides are identical. Ex. Coll. William
Spratling, Taxco.

183. PRE-TOTONAC RABBIT—STONE—VERA CRUZ—
CA. 700—H. 17.8 cm. (7″)

To these people and to the Aztecs, the "rabbit" was the name of
a day, in divination associated with good luck, fertility, and the
god Mayauel. It symbolized the maguey plant, important for
fibres, spines, and intoxicating wine. The worship of rabbit
gods was widespread and was associated with the harvest and
the moon. This figure's ears are glyphs, and the eyes were once
inlaid. Found at Papalpan, Mislanta.

184. TOTONAC HACHA—ANDESITE—VERA CRUZ—
CA. 1000—H. 24.1 cm. (9½″)

This *hacha* is not as flat, nor well-worked, as No. 182. It was
found in the El Tajin area.

185. TOTONAC FIGURINE—CLAY—VERA CRUZ—1000
TO CONQUEST—H. 13.6 cm. (5⅜″)

Here is a mother suckling her child. There are vestiges of color
and bitumen. Found near Tenexpan.

186. PRE-TOTONAC HEAD—STONE—VERA CRUZ—DATING
UNKNOWN—H. 19.8 cm. (7⅞″)

How often have we found this subject among the art of a military nation—the dying warrior? This is an interesting sculpture. Found at Xotla, Axocuapan.

187. TOTONAC MASK—STONE—VERA CRUZ—CA. 1000
—H. 17.5 cm. (6⅞″)

It is believed that these masks were applied to shrouds, and not
used as the masks of Africa were.

182

183

184

185

186

187

188. TOTONAC YOKE—CARVED METADIORITE—VERA CRUZ—CA. 900—L. 39.2 cm. (15½")

The purpose of these strange horseshoe-shaped carvings known as "yokes" remains conjectural. They are found in graves, but they are said to have been used in penitential ceremonies or placed around the neck of sacrificial victims. Our theory is the ball game where they are shown on wall paintings. The carving is in the form of a stylized frog. Found at Papalpan.

189. TOTONAC PALMATE—ANDESITE—VERA CRUZ— CA. 500—H. 39.3 cm. (15½")

Stone sculptures which spread out fanshape towards the top are called "palmates" and are found only in the orbit of the Tajin civilization. Their significance is unknown. The carving of this skeletal form is richly ornate. On the reverse side is an unusual design which includes four naked footprints.

190. TOTONAC WHISTLE—CLAY—VERA CRUZ—500-700—H. 31.3 cm. (12⅜")

This elaborately decorated cusp-footed figure is a pleasant sounding whistle. It was probably used religiously. It is partially painted with bitumen (pitch) and haematite (red oxide of iron) used as coloring for ceramics and as the Indians' war paint. Cinnabar (red sulphide of mercury) is more rare, but its vermilion color also appears as decoration. Las Remojadas style.

191. TOTONAC HEAD—CLAY—VERA CRUZ—CA. 800— H. 8.7 cm. (3½")

The mysterious smile of these heads becomes an expression of ecstasy when the whole figure—with the head thrown back as in a state of rapture—is viewed. They show certain affinities with Maya ceramics. These heads, as well as full figures (No. 192 below), are two-toned whistles—one a whole tone below middle C, the other a half tone above.

192. TOTONAC FIGURINE—CLAY—VERA CRUZ— CA. 800—H. 21.6 cm. (8½")

This is one of nine *caritas sonrientes* (smiling faces) with full figure which we found at Tenexpan in one cache. They are all of different size, form, and decoration, deviating from theory as they are supposed to be mold made. The heads have been known and admired for some time, but it was only recently that complete figures were found. They seem to depict dancers, but other authorities have suggested they are victims chosen for sacrificial death and under the influence of some drug.

193. OLMEC FIGURE—STONE—LA VENTA—500 B.C.-A.D. 1— H. 15.9 cm. (6¼")

This small figure is in the style of the great monolithic stone sculptures of Tabasco although it does not have the helmet-like headdress.

194. OLMEC HEAD—GREEN SCHIST—EASTERN OAXACA— CA. 500 B.C.—H. 14.8 cm. (5⅞")

This is an example of the features employed by these people when they did not portray the "baby face."

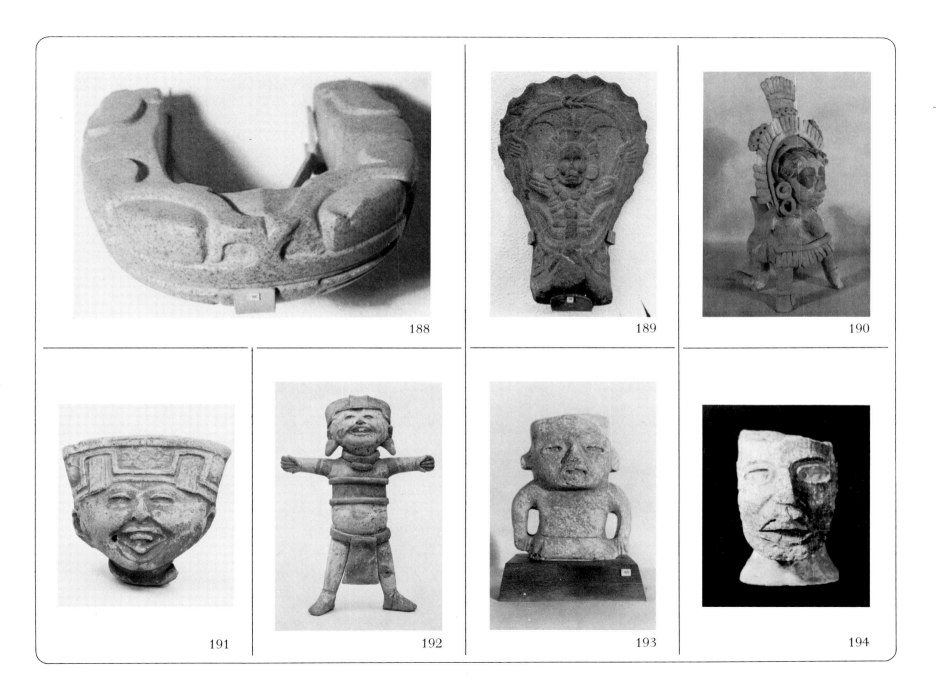

188

189

190

191

192

193

194

195. TARASCAN BOWL—POTTERY—COLIMA—0-500—
H. 19 cm. (7½")

This bowl bears the design of the peyote, a spineless cactus from which was made the exhilarating drug used during ceremonials.

196. TARASCAN FIGURE—MODELED CLAY—NAYARIT—
0-500—H. 55.1 cm. (21¾")

This figure from the Mexpan area was found in *tiro y boveda* (deep shaft with chambers at the bottom), at a depth of 16 meters, with skeletal remains. This male figure, in mint condition, is one of a pair. The *falda* (skirt) on the female was broken. Its discovery in the shaft burial forms the subject of a booklet by Dr. José Corona Nunez, and there is a model of this burial in the Tepic Museum.

197. TARASCAN BOWL—BURNISHED CLAY—COLIMA—
0-500—H. 21.6 cm. (8½")

These parrot-footed tripod bowls are invariably of more or less the same pumpkin-shaped, voluted design. The neatly turned rim is noteworthy. Found near Buena Vista.

198. TARASCAN FIGURINE—MODELED CLAY—MICHOACAN—ARCHAIC PERIOD—H. 11.3 cm. (4⅜")

These archaic figurines are extremely rare. This example possesses great vitality. Vestiges of color.

199. TARASCAN STATUETTE—MODELED CLAY—JALISCO
—0-500—H. 24.4 cm. (9⅝")

This painted figure, found near Ixtlan, has cranial deformation and wears nose plug, bracelets, necklace, and other ornaments. This collection includes examples of the various types of this jewelry.

200. TARASCAN STATUETTE—MODELED CLAY—JALISCO
—0-500—H. 28.5 cm. (11¼")

This stylized figure wears the familiar padded and decorated shoulder throw and seems to be blowing a horn. The shape of the head is in the characteristic Jalisco form.

201. TARASCAN STATUETTE—MODELED CLAY—NAYARIT
—ARCHAIC PERIOD—H. 15.8 cm. (6¼")

This figurine, found at the earliest level at Las Penitas, is aberrant. Although the "shovel heads" appear regularly, we cannot account for the Oriental type of veil, pendant on the face, and the form of the body.

195

196

197

198

199

200

201

202. TARASCAN PETROGLYPH—STONE—MICHOACAN—
CA. 800—L. 45.2 cm. (17½")

This stone carving was part of a temple stairway. The figure on the right represents Ehecatl, god of the winds, and the other Tlaloc, the goddess of fertility.

203. TARASCAN STATUETTE—MODELED CLAY—NAYARIT—ARCHAIC PERIOD—H. 13.6 cm. (5⅜")

This warrior with round headdress—a form of armor, as these people also used quilted cotton armor—shield, and *atl-atl* (spear thrower) is a beautiful small sculpture. Dr. Karl With declared it "by a genius."

204. TWO TARASCAN FIGURES—MODELED CLAY—NAYARIT—0-500—H. 14.2 cm. (5⅝")

This pair of seated figures portrays grotesque high humor in their desolation. We cherish them as the "mourners." The sculptor takes liberties with the length of the limbs to achieve compact composition. Red burnish. Cf. Feuchtwanger, *Art of Ancient Mexico*, pl. 74. Gift of that fine dealer and our friend, Mr. Edward Primus, Beverly Hills, California.

205. TARASCAN FIGURINE—MODELED CLAY—JALISCO—0-500—H. 13.6 cm. (5⅜")

This painted figurine of mother and child, also found at Ixtlan, wears the same shoulder dress as No. 200.

206. TARASCAN DOG—MODELED CLAY—COLIMA—0-500—H. 22.2 cm. (8¾")

These dogs are depicted playing, chasing their tails, and in many other endearing, amusing attitudes. The Tarascans were not trammeled by religion as much as were their neighbors to the east and south. Their art was largely representational and of a naïve humor. Hence we do not concur with the theory, based on the finding of archaic human-masked dog figures, that these were to be companions after death. They appear to be companions during life. But the Tarascans ate dogs.

207. TWO TARASCAN CELTS—GRANITE—NAYARIT—CA. 900—L. 10.9 and 7.1 cm. (4¼" and 2¾")

Here are two examples of the elaborately carved stone celts the Tarascan used, depicting realistic animals.

202

203

204

205

206

207

208. MIXTEC FACE—CLAY—VALLEY OF OAXACA—
CA. 1100—H. 15.4 cm. (6⅛″)

This expressively modeled face is from Monte Alban IV. Vestiges of color remain.

209. ZAPOTEC LINTEL—STONE—OAXACA—CA. 700—
L. 1 m., 72.7 cm. (68″)

This lintel is in the style of Monte Alban III. It shows a coyote with an anthropomorphic body, which represents the patron of the dance, and two highly stylized birds, the masters of music. So this lintel may well have been over the doorway of the Temple of the Dance. Traces of light stucco remain.

210. MIXTEC STATUE—BASALTIC LAVA—OAXACA—
CA. 1500—H. 32.7 cm. (12⅞″)

This figure of a warrior carrying a club is pre-Conquest. The volcanic rock is called tuffa stone.

211. TOLTEC-MAYA BALL COURT MARKER—STONE—
900-1000—D. 30.5 cm. (12″)

From the famous ball court at Chichen Itza, this carving was on the east bench center panel and was part of the procession arrangement. It shows the Toltec tightly curled tip of the speech scroll in contrast to the Classic Maya version, which is square or open. Cf. Proshourishoff, "Study of Classic Maya Culture," Carnegie Publ. 593, Washington, 1950.

212. MIXTEC URN—CLAY—OAXACA—CA. 1300—
H. 23.1 cm. (9⅛″)

Effigy funerary urns are typical of this district. They feature anthropomorphic and zoomorphic figures, behind which are vessels in which were placed ashes of the bones of the deceased for secondary burial. They were covered with a red wash. This is Monte Alban V. While cleaning this piece, we found in its container the small jade carving, No. 77-81, on page 167.

213. ZAPOTEC STELE—CARVED MARBLE—OAXACA— CA. 1000—H. 70.3 cm. (27⅝″)

This represents two chiefs negotiating as evidenced by the "voice scrolls" emanating from their mouths, precisely as in the "funnies" today. It is believed from the cut of their hair and clothing that the individual in the long robe is Olmec and the other Zapotec. This was originally painted.

214. ZAPOTEC URN—CLAY—OAXACA—CA. 400—
H. 23.2 cm. (9⅛″)

This is a much earlier example of the same type as No. 212. It dates from Monte Alban III and was found near Mitla. These two pieces are the result of years of searching, as they, although over 1000 years apart, are two of the smallest urns of their type ever found. He wears the strange mouth mask of the rain god who is also characterized in Maya iconography by a long hooked nose, Cocijo.

208

209

210

211

212

213

214

215. MAYA STELE—YELLOW LIMESTONE—CHIAPAS—
CA. 600—L. 60.2 cm. (23¾″)

This truly elegant, graceful carving, bearing a glyph, was found at Palenque with others of the same type.

216. MAYA FIGURE—HAND-MODELED, FINE-TEXTURED CLAY—ISLAND OF JAINA—CA. 700—H. 24.7 cm. (5⅜″)

This type of clay figure at its finest, reinforces the Maya claim to pre-eminence in New World art. These were burial offerings found in the cemeteries on the island of Jaina, off the coast of Campeche. Their realistic style is reminiscent of the beautiful Greek Tanagras similarly used. Note the Maya physiognomy. Traces of paint. Classic Period.

217. MAYA FIGURE—HAND-MODELED, FINE-TEXTURED CLAY—ISLAND OF JAINA—CA. 700—H. 29.6 cm. (11¾″)

This figure, found with No. 216 above, strangely has the face and dress of the Olmec. The appliqué of his heavy ornamentation is unusual. Vestiges of color remain.

218. MAYA STELE—MARBLE—CAMPECHE—CA. 700— H. 72.4 cm. (28½″)

This is the upper portion of a stele of a life-sized figure found near Holactun. The entire piece is full-length, but it was broken in two just below the face, discernible in the lower left hand corner. This upper portion shows the face and the elaborate Maya headdress customarily depicted for these dignitaries. It is believed that these steles were intentionally broken along with most of the possessions of the ancient Maya in the observance of their religious time cycles.

219. TWO MAYA STATUES—CLAY—CHIAPAS—400-500 —H. 35.1 and 30.7 cm. (13¾″ and 12⅛″)

In the northeast corner of Chiapas, adjacent to the Guatemalan border, survives a handful of Maya Indians known as the Lacandon. Here our friend Giles Healey discovered the now famous ancient paintings of Bonampak. These Indians still make pilgrimages to the ruins of Yaxchilan and Bonampak to offer prayers and burn incense in the temples of their ancestors. When we obtained these two figures several years ago from this area, these potent demoniac effigies, with their flamboyant decoration, posed a stylistic problem. They were unlike any previously known. However, we were delighted to find in the *Illustrated London News*, January 27, 1962, a full page illustration of an identical figure found at Tikal, about 100 miles away, by Mr. William R. Coe, of the University of Pennsylvania's expedition. It was in an Early Classic tomb.

220. MAYA BOWL—PAINTED CLAY—NORTHERN HONDURAS—CA. 500—H. 7.3 cm. (2⅞″)

This polychrome jar has four seated priests in full regalia painted upon it. It was found at the Ulua Valley near Copan and is of the Late Classic Period.

215

216

217

218

219

220

The locus of this area is in the Andes extending for nearly 3600 miles along the western length of South America. However, before reaching Peru we must pass through the tropical countries to its north. Concerning this north, we are not yet able to correlate the art styles of these sections with the Peruvian styles or with each other. We know that these Indians were ignorant of the wheel, including the potter's wheel, they had no bow, and they were illiterate. But their works, which we shall indicate, show that they were possessed of fanatical religious beliefs and, certain of their skills, nurtured by these beliefs, established their eminence.

Starting in what presently is Costa Rica and continuing through the mountainous sections and coastal plains of Panama, Colombia, Venezuela, and Ecuador we find no cultural unity. Tropical peoples seldom build with permanent materials, and here the highlands, in close juxtaposition, were uniformly influenced. So there are no ruins of buildings or temples, built of wood and long since decayed. From the *Nicoya* River area of Costa Rica come fine decorated ceramics, carved stone column-like statues, gold ornaments, and the characteristic ceremonial grinding stones—*metates* (No. 232).

The *Cocle* and *Chiriqui* graves of Panama yield multicolor plates and bowls, stone artifacts, and gold objects of excellent quality (No. 226). In Colombia the greatest technical achievements were in metallurgy. Existing gold ornaments and figures are superb. The political and religious systems in ancient Colombia, particularly the concept of gods, show many parallels to the Aztecs and Maya but otherwise compare closely with the Central Andean pattern prior to the superimposition of the Inca structure. The main cultures here were: *San Agustin*, noted for stone carving and the subterranean stone-lined temples and tombs; *Tierra-Dentro*, noted for its painted subterranean burial chambers; *Quimbaya*, noted for the master goldsmiths of the Americas; *Sinu, Upper Cauca, Marino, Mosquito*, quite archaic; *Tairano*, noted for elaborate village sites, vaults, ceremonial courts and other structures of dressed stone; and finally the *Chibcha*, who inhabited the large highland basin around Bogota and whom the conquering Spaniards estimated as 4,000,000 people in their time. Despite minor stylistic differences, we may consider the Andes of Venezuela linked to Colombia.

In Ecuador, the *Esmeraldas* (No. 228) and *Manabi* (No. 230) cultures were amazingly advanced for tropical forest dwellers. Their affiliations with Central America and Peru would imply wide-scale trade. We know that these people were navigators and made distant journeys on their large sailing rafts of balsa wood. They were also stone carvers (No. 227). Little is yet known of the *Carchi, Loja, Canar*, and *Azuay*, who worked metal and whose pottery shows a mixture of styles (Nos. 229, 231).

And now we enter Peru. When in 1532, Francisco Pizarro with his Conquistadores sailed here from Panama, he destroyed the great Inca Empire, whose dynasty was then only 123 years old. The Incas were the first to integrate this vast area, larger than our entire Atlantic seaboard. But many rather advanced civilizations had been built up in its mountain fastnesses, its high plateaus, and its habitable fertile valleys during the previous 2500 years. They have left us their mute record in the ruins of their temples and buildings, their roads, their pottery, metal work, and their textiles. Although there is no common denominator for the styles of the various Andean cultures, there is a framework of Andean characteristics. We shall use the datings of Professor Wendell C. Bennett of Yale University as we follow these cultures.

Period I (1200-400 B.C.). Earliest ceramics, corn, mosaic, true weaving, and other elements. All are linked by the original *Chavin* horizon style, characterized by a highly stylized feline design on stone carving, ceramics, gold, and textiles (No. 233). The same jaguar motif also appears in Mexico, but the Mexican version, with its peculiarly high arched lips, seems unrelated to the Andean. The Chavin feline design persistently survives for over two thousand years in Andean decoration. The valley of Chavin could not have supported a large permanent population and was probably a center for religious pilgrimages which could explain the wide spread of the symbolic Chavin feline design. Chavin was the fountainhead of ritual art. The isolated site of Chavin de Hauntar lies in the Callejon de Huaylas basin, and one of this area's frequent landslides, in recent years, covered most of the ruins of this most elaborate center. There existed other smaller First Period centers such as *Cupisnique, Ancon*, and *Chicama*.

Period II (400 B.C.-A.D. 400). Technological innovations in building, irrigation, weaving, ceramics, metallurgy, and great changes in

ANCIENT CULTURES OF THE CENTRAL ANDES
REGIONAL AND TIME DIVISIONS

North Coast	Callejon de Huaylas	Central Coast	South Coast	Cuzco	Titicaca	Periods	
Inca						VI	1438-1532 A.D.
Chimu	Huamachuco	Chancay	Ica	Early Inca	Collao	V	1300-1438 A.D.
Tiahuanaco						IV	1000-1300 A.D.
Mochica	Recuay	Interlocking	Nazca		Pucara	III	400-1000 A.D.
Salinar	White-on-Red	White-on-Red	Paracas Nec	Chanapata	Chiripa	II	400 B.C.-400 A.D.
Chavin						I	1200-400 B.C.

(Adapted with permission of American Museum of Natural History)

ceramic development. The *Salinar* culture prevailed on the North Coast, with its small-figure modeling on vessels. In the arid south are located the two great *Paracas* cemeteries—designated *Cavernas* and *Necropolis* (III Period). In this region, where rains do not fall for years on end, and seemingly unfit for human habitation, were found deep chambered graves in which are perfectly preserved wooden objects, great quantities of textiles woven in many different advanced techniques, basketry, and ceramics of variegated styles (Nos. 240, 243).

Period III (A.D. 400-1000). This period dates the mastery of technical development and produced the finest examples of ceramics and weaving. Independent local cultures developed agriculture, animal husbandry, architecture, the production of luxury goods and of crafts to an apogee. The Mochicas on the North Coast built pyramids and had a faithfully realistic art style. The stirrup-spout jars with painted representations of warriors and jaguars (No. 241), a holdover from the Chavin, as well as their realistic portrait jars are well known (No. 244). The mummy bundles of Paracas Necropolis, referred to above, are attributed to this period. Their textiles—turbans, shirts, mantles, and ornamentation—were of superb quality. The *Nazca* of the South Coast, like Necropolis, emphasized fine weaving (No. 246), neglected architecture, and produced thin polychrome painted ceramics in as many as ten colors, decorated by complicated stylized designs of anthropomorphic monsters, felines with undecipherable appendages (Nos. 248, 249, 250). The third important culture of this time span was the *Recuay*, which centered in the Callejon de Huaylas basin and built large stone slab subterranean houses and temples. Their pottery is rather chaotic, often painted three-color negative and of elaborate surface pattern and complex form.

Period IV (A.D. 1000-1300). This time span is dominated by the *Tiahuanaco* culture. The source of these people appears to have been around the elaborate site of Tiahuanaco, which lies in the bleak highlands on the Bolivian side of the Lake Titicaca basin. Here stood a huge, stone-faced, stepped pyramid and an immense area of construction units. How did these people ever transport in the rarified air of 12,000 feet the monolithic Gateway to the Sun? Tiahuanaco culture spread, probably by military conquest, through the Peruvian highlands to the coast and Northern Chile. The Peruvian and Bolivian manifestations of the Tiahuanaco culture are clearly related, although neither is directly derived from the other. These people were excellent stone masons and carvers of stone (No. 245). Their ceramics and textiles show a strong uniformity of style (No. 247). Tiahuanaco expansion eliminated the peaceful Nazcas of the south, who never reappear; it obliterated Central Coast cultures; but in the north, although the Mochicas were temporarily eclipsed, they soon revived and reappeared as the Chimu.

Period V (A.D. 1300-1438). The Tiahuanaco expansion probably coalesced with little political unity, and its breakdown was rapid early in this period. It was followed by a re-emergence of regional cultures. Although it had been disruptive, techniques and skills had not been lost. The new emphasis was now definitely on political organization. Populations reshifted into larger habitation centers. Fortifications were built and garrisoned. The crafts were still produced competently and in quantity, but quality and artistic inspiration were lacking.

The *Icas* of the South Coast continued traditional weaving but reduced the design to repetitive small geometric elements which also appear on their ceramics (No. 238). On the other hand, building activity was accelerated. The Central Coast valleys were dominated by the *Chancay*, apparently well-organized politically. In both form and design, Chancay ceramics are unlike those of the major Peruvian cultures (No. 235). They seem closer to the Northern Andes and the Amazon basin.

As mentioned before, the Mochica culture of the North Coast was not totally obliterated by the Tiahuanaco expansion. It now re-emerges as *Chimu*—old Mochica modified by Tiahuanaco influence. Chimu political organization was extensive, and large city units were built. Every available hectare of land was cultivated by intensive irrigation. The ceremonial city of Chan Chan, covering over eight square miles, was built with its pyramids, houses, reservoirs, and extensive cemeteries. Chimu ceramics are predominantly of smoked black ware, reminiscent of Etruscan Bucchero ware (Nos. 236, 237). The stirrup-spout container, reflecting the earlier Mochica, was still a favorite, but the art lacked realism. Great quantities of textiles were produced. Feather mosaic pieces appear. Copper knives, axes and clubs, as well as gold and silver goblets, breastplates and ear cylinders were made (No. 234). Then, all of these people were subjugated by the invading Inca, down from the high Andes.

Period VI (A.D. 1438-1532). The huge *Inca* Empire, with its center in the valley of Cuzco, stretched from Ecuador to Chile and was completely totalitarian. Everything was owned or managed by the state. The vast territory of the Inca was welded into collectivist lines and founded on conquest. Once a people was subdued, the process of incorporation was systematically applied. Their language was supplanted by the national tongue, Quechua. Important hostages and the most sacred of their religious objects were taken to the Inca capital of Cuzco. Roads to link them with the system were built, and their area was militarily occupied. If they continued rebellious, entire populations were removed to other sections. Obedient labor and service were required by the state, which fed the population from national granaries. In contradistinction to the northern area, the white potato, not maize, was the food staple. The guinea pig was the principal meat source. Unlike the Indians to the north, they abhorred dog meat. The Inca Empire was based on intensive agriculture. Today, there may still be seen miles of terracing for agriculture on the sides of the most precipitous mountains.

Generally the features of Inca culture were based upon past developments. The great genius of the Inca was in political organization, not art. The caste system was inviolate. The small elite of the Inca and the royal family, with, at a lower level, the rulers of conquered areas, were a complete autocracy. The commoners had no escape from their drab position. They were mere herds of labor. The Incas are famed for the quantity and variety of their stone construction. Besides their network of roads, sites such as Machu Picchu, Cuzco, Ollantaytambo, Sacsayhauman, etc. show that these people moved monolithic pink granite blocks over mountains and rivers and dressed them to precision fits with abrasives. This technique was only approached in the Khmer monuments (Angkor Wat) in Cambodia. Unquestionably, religion held a powerful grasp. The cult of the dead was prominently reflected in the burial practices. The concept of *huaca*, special spiritual power, was attributed to all sacred places and is still used today in reference to ancient remains and artifacts. Inca ceramic shapes are highly standardized. The Inca urn, resembling the Greek aryballos, is characteristic (No. 242). The design on ceramics is generally polychrome geometric with occasional representations of butterflies, bees, animals, and block-like humans. Weaving was now generally less ornate. Copper was worked (No. 239). The last Inca, Atahualpa, had vast treasures of gold and silver ornaments; walls and furniture were sheathed in gold, inlaid with emeralds; table service was of gold; and the Spaniards report that his garden contained delicate butterflies and beds of flowers all of beautifully cast gold. These were duly melted into bullion and shipped to Spain.

Unlike certain peoples to their north, the ancient Peruvian lacked any form of writing or a recorded calendar. But it would be difficult to find anywhere else in the world higher standards of technical excellence in ceramics and textiles. However, in spite of the great variety of subject matter used in the decoration, one is often struck by the monotony of the later product. Spontaneity is not its forte. It seems to have been put together by established formula. Only the earlier pieces, as a rule, possess vigor and originality. The Inca Empire quickly perished when Pizarro captured their Sun King, Atahualpa.

Most of the other pre-Inca archaeological cultures in northwestern *Argentina* and northern *Chile* can be assigned to Periods II, IV, and V in the Central Andean sequence. The early period, best presented by the *Barreales* culture, is rather crude. The middle period, dominated by the *Calchaqui*, left some interesting, large polychrome urns, ollas, and decorated bowls, as well as bronze plaques. The cultures of the late period, before the Inca invasion, including *Atacameno*, reduced craftsmanship to the utilitarian level.

To the east, the great expanse of tropical jungle was an effective block to the expansion of the Inca Empire. There has been little archaeological work in Amazonia. The few known sites are widely scattered, and we shall not go into *Marajao, Mirakanguera,* or baroque *Santarem* here. Following are examples of the works of these people.

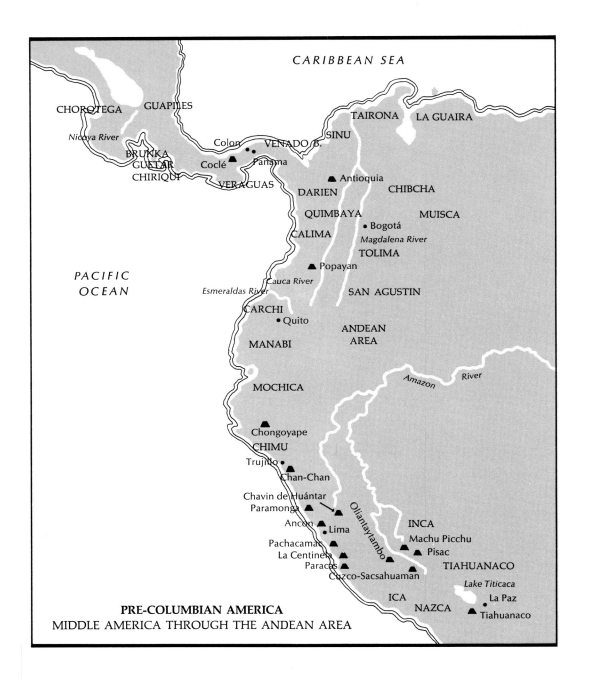

CARIBBEAN SEA

CHOROTEGA GUAPILES

TAIRONA   LA GUAIRA

SINU

Nicoya River

Colon VENADO B.

BRUNKA
GUETAR
CHIRIQUI

Coclé   Panama

VERAGUAS

Antioquia

DARIEN   CHIBCHA

QUIMBAYA   MUISCA

CALIMA   • Bogotá

Magdalena River

TOLIMA

Popayan

Cauca River

PACIFIC
OCEAN

Esmeraldas River

SAN AGUSTIN

CARCHI

• Quito

ANDEAN
AREA

MANABI

Amazon   River

MOCHICA

Chongoyape

CHIMU

Trujillo •

Chan-Chan

Chavin de Huántar
Paramonga

Oliantayambo

Ancon

INCA

• Lima

Machu Picchu

Pachacamac

La Centinela   • Pisac

Paracas

TIAHUANACO

Cuzco-Sacsahuaman

Lake Titicaca

ICA   • La Paz

NAZCA

Tiahuanaco

PRE-COLUMBIAN AMERICA
MIDDLE AMERICA THROUGH THE ANDEAN AREA

226. CHIRIQUI INCENSE BURNER—CLAY—NORTHERN
PANAMA—1000(?)—H. 18.3 cm. (7¼″)

The legs of this tripod, in the form of sharks, contain pellets
which rattle. Incense was burned in the body. One may visualize a shaman shaking these rattles of the incense burning vessel
and invoking his incantations.

227. MANABI THRONE—STONE—ECUADOR—
PRE-CONQUEST—W. 67.3 cm. (26½″)

This is an unusual example of this monumental form, reminiscent of the stonework of Central America. An incised example
of these U-shaped stone thrones resting on a crouching human
figure is rare.

228. ESMERALDAS PORTRAIT VESSEL—CLAY—SOUTHERN
COLOMBIA—1000-1300—H. 16.7 cm. (6⅝″)

While the headdress and decoration on this three-color, nega-
tive-painted ware is reminiscent of Central America, it is definitely related to the portrait heads further south, notably
Mochica. The "C Y" pattern persists from Costa Rica to Ecuador.

229. LOJA AX HEAD—BRONZE—ECUADOR—CA. 1000—
L. 12.8 cm. (5″)

This ax head was found by Dr. Carl. Nigel who has been inves-
tigating the little known Loja culture.

230. MANABI VESSEL—CLAY—ECUADOR—CA. 1000—
L. 14.5 cm. (5¾″)

The Manabi were stone carvers. The form and incising here
might be compared to the Tiahuanaco of Bolivia as this ceramic gives the impression of stoneware. Ex. Coll. Carl Nigel.

231. LOJA KNIFE—BRONZE—ECUADOR—CA. 1200—
L. 44.4 cm. (17½″)

Found with No. 229 above, this is an unusually large example
of the conventional blade.

226

227

228

229

230

231

232. NICOYA METATE—BASALTIC LAVA—COSTA RICA—
PRE-CONQUEST—L. 64.5 cm. (25⅜")

Small tables—*metates*—have long been ubiquitous in every
household, for grinding corn for the daily tortillas. This ceremonial type is in the form of a jaguar and is concave for the use
of a pestle—*mano*. This jaguar is adorned with a diamond
pattern, continuing on to the tail, which forms a convenient
handle.

233. CHAVIN HEAD—STONE—CHAVIN DE HUANTAR—
1200-800 B.C.—H. 10.3 cm. (4⅛")

This is the story of collecting. For a decade we vainly searched
for one of the rare examples of South America's earliest civilization, the Chavin horizon, delineating the incipient feline
style, copied for the succeeding centuries. Eventually one was
found, not in Peru or abroad, but in a New York City collection. Note that the face of the feline monster has protruding
fangs and eyes which can be read as belonging to a profile view
and a frontal view simultaneously, as in the animal forms of
Chinese ritual bronzes. Exhibited: Museum of Primitive Art,
"Gods with Fangs," New York, 1961.

234. TWO CHIMU BEAKERS—SILVER—NORTH COAST PERU
—1300-1438—H. 15.4 cm. (6⅛")

These were found at Chan Chan. The silver was hammered in
one piece in repoussé and then clinched.

235. CHANCAY VESSEL—CLAY—CENTRAL COAST PERU—
1300-1438—H. 30.1 cm. (11⅞")

In both form and design Chancay vessels differ from the major
Peruvian cultures. They appear closer to the work from the
northern Andes and the Amazonian basin. This is in the form
of a seated man.

236. CHIMU DOUBLE SPOUT JAR—CLAY—NORTH COAST
PERU—1300-1438—H. 20.1 cm. (8")

This is a mint example of the characteristic smoked black-ware,
decorated with a pressed design. Between the double spouts is
a modeled bridge. There were reasons for the stirrup-spout
form. The stirrup handle and tubes afford easy pouring. Also,
evaporation of the water, so precious on the arid coast, was reduced by condensation inside these tubes and by the small
vents.

237. CHIMU SINGLE SPOUT JAR—CLAY—NORTH COAST
PERU—1300-1438—H. 19.7 cm. (7⅞")

The mold-made warrior on this double vessel, single spout
stirrup jar carries a club.

238. ICA BOWL—CLAY—SOUTH COAST PERU—1300-1438—
H. 15.1 cm. (6")

These people copied their ceramic painted styles directly from
their textile patterns. Ex. Coll. Soldi.

232

233

234

235

236

237

238

239. INCA KNIFE—BRONZE—PERUVIAN ANDES—1438-1532—
L. 10.3 cm. (4″)

Another knife, closely resembling this, was also found at
Machu Picchu by Dr. Hiram Bingham and is illustrated in
P. Kelemen, *Medieval American Art*, New York: The Macmillan Co., 1956, pl. 205. This is thin and evidently once had a
sharp cutting edge. The figure of a fisherman drawing in his
net is lively and lifelike.

240. PARACAS LEEBOARD—WOOD—SOUTH COAST PERU—
CA. 400—L. 247.4 cm. (97⅜″)

Leeboards were used as rudders. The intricacy of the carving
shows that this one could not have been utilitarian, hence,
was ceremonial. It is of a very hard wood and carved out of one
piece. Only in a cemetery like Paracas Cavernas, or possibly in
Egypt, will arid climate so preserve wood.

241. MOCHICA WHISTLING JAR—CLAY—NORTH COAST
PERU—400-1000—H. 19.3 cm. (7⅝″)

This double black-ware jar half in the form of a seal is also a
whistle. When liquids are poured from it, it emits a mournful
sound. This is the ancestor of the Chimu black-ware Nos. 236
and 237.

242. INCA URN—CLAY—CENTRAL COAST PERU—1438-1532
—H. 21.8 cm. (8⅝″)

Note the resemblance to the Greek aryballos. Inca ceramics
were made in only a few shapes distinctive for their dignity
and beauty of proportion. Most decoration was geometric.

243. PARACAS BOWL—CLAY—SOUTH COAST PERU—
400-1000—H. 14.2 cm. (5⅝″)

This handsome red slip bowl with its post-fired painted stripes
is particularly interesting for the magic bean warriors painted
on it and its pair of modeled jaguars. It was found in a subterranean room at Paracas Necropolis.

244. MOCHICA PORTRAIT HEAD—CLAY—NORTH COAST
PERU—400-1000—H. 20.4 cm. (8″)

A fine example of realistic portraiture typical of this culture,
these heads are distinctively Mochican.

239

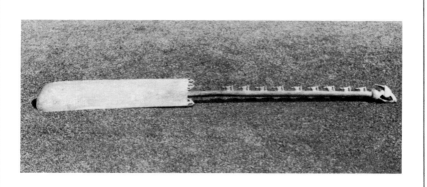

240

242

241

243

244

245. TWO TIAHUANACO FIGURINES—STONE—PERUVIAN ANDES—1000-1300—H. 16 cm. (6¼″)

These carved stone figures, probably religious amulets, were taken from a burial near Cuzco.

246. NAZCA FABRIC—SLIT TAPESTRY WEAVE—SOUTH COAST PERU—400-1000—L. 61.2 cm. (24⅛″)

This slit tapestry weave fabric has a cotton warp and wool weft. The preservation of the extraordinary brilliant coloring is a tribute to the dyes employed so long ago. Illustrated: Wendell Clark Bennett, *Ancient Arts of the Andes*, Museum of Modern Art, 1954, pl. 70. Ex. Coll. John Wise, New York.

247. TIAHUANACO STIRRUP JAR—CLAY—SOUTH COAST PERU—1000-1300—H. 15.2 cm. (6″)

Extremely amusing is this stirrup jar with its little man apparently in tears. This is coastal, not the Tiahuanaco style of the highland Bolivian culture, and shows an admixture of local style—probably Nazca.

248. NAZCA STIRRUP JAR—CLAY—SOUTH COAST PERU—CA. 1100—H. 16.2 cm. (6⅜″)

The angular stylization of the fantastic animals decorating this double spouted vessel reveals considerable Tiahuanaco influence, which places it in Period IV. It has a glaze.

249. NAZCA FIGURINE—CLAY—SOUTH COAST PERU—400-1000—L. 19.8 cm. (7¾″)

This modeled, painted quail is quite realistic and amusing.

250. NAZCA BOWL—CLAY—SOUTH COAST PERU—400-1000—H. 8 cm. (3⅛″)

Here is a characteristic bell-shaped bowl of fine thin quality. The polychrome representational decoration is typical.

245

247

246

248

249

250

142

For centuries the imagination and cupidity of man has been aroused by the stories of Eldorado. The legendary Manoa, "with golden roofs and streets paved with gold" has never been found. Pizarro's lieutenant, Mojano, failed in his quest for the treasure of the last Inca of Cuzco.

But we do know that from the coasts of the New World whole fleets of galleons sailed for the ports of Spain laden with precious ingots on which the seal of the Catholic king had decreed the death of a magnificent and authentic civilization. For centuries past, these ingots had been diadems and funerary masks, pectorals and sceptres, armor, vessels, girdles, idols, and jewels beautifully fashioned and now fallen to the crucibles of the rapacious Conquistadores, intent on a systematic work of plunder and destruction.

Here is an attempt to show examples from as many cultures as possible. These objects were acquired in the various countries between Mexico and Chile. There is no firm basis for classifying some of these pieces with certainty by culture or fixed chronological periods. We have classified them, with certain misgivings, to the areas from which they were obtained. Very broadly, all date from A.D. 400 to the Conquest. Provenance is shown wherever possible.

This gold was worked in the most refined techniques and is of high artistic merit. These artifacts cannot be considered folk art as they were manufactured for the aristocrats of their day. Furthermore, they represent a wide range in time and space, and they reflect many and varied stylistic traditions.

The skills in fabricating gold are truly surprising in view of the general simplicity of other aspects of many of the cultures. The available metals were gold, or the gold-copper alloy called *tumbaga*. These were worked by hammering, repoussé, filigree, embossing, plating, gilding, inlaying, sheathing, engraving, welding, and soldering. Some of these techniques required absolute heat control and transcended what was possible in Europe at this time. Exquisite *cire perdue* castings were common. Variations were achieved by joining metals of slightly different composition. Also, both copper and bronze ornaments and implements were produced.

Briefly, the indigenous techniques of goldwork started with primitive hammering. Later, gold was melted in stone crucibles using forced draft provided by blowing through tubes or cast in open or closed molds. A more complicated process was that of hollow casting by *cire perdue*. In this method a modeled core, made of clay and powdered charcoal, was covered by a thin coating of wax and finally by a shell of clay and powdered charcoal. Two openings were left so that the molten gold ran in one and the wax out the other. Ergo, the name *cire perdue*—lost wax.

Ornamental elements were attached to some pieces by welding or using some other metal as solder, which, by definition, has a lower melting point than the pieces to be joined. Metal, wood, shell, or stone were sheathed with gold foil (77-41). Heavy gold plating was used (77-59). A mercury-gold technique was used (77-61). A veneer of fine gold leaf was applied to a casting of base metal (77-58). The coloring technique called *mise en couleur* was used on alloys of copper and gold to imitate gilding (77-62). In this method, application of an acid to the alloy eats away the copper and floats the gold.

Tumbaga is an alloy of gold and silver/copper and varies greatly in gold content (77-60, 77-63). Also, gold was cold hammered into sheets which could then be cut out into shapes or embossed, probably with a bone tool on a leather anvil, or designed in repoussé by hammering over carved molds (77-12). Yes, these primitive people evolved many techniques!

Jade is a generic term used to designate several distinct mineral species widely used in primitive cultures for such simple utilitarian objects as celts or knives and in some advanced civilizations for decorative pieces as jewels, ceremonial objects, and carvings. Montezuma, the Aztec emperor, told Cortéz that jades were his most precious possession and that he valued them more than gold: "Each stone is worth two loads of gold." A Maya jade, inscribed with a date, is known to have been cherished above ground for fully one thousand years before it was interred with its then owner.

Two distinct mineral species became associated with the term jade: jadeite (and its congeners diopside-jadeite and chloromelanite) and nephrite. Jadeite is similar to the Asiatic mineral we know so well today but shows significant chemical differences and a much wider variety in color and texture. Suffice it to say here that jades vary greatly in texture and that colors are both clear and mottled, ranging from whites, through celadon, emerald, to blue-greys, ivory green, and almost black.

We are indebted to Dr. Alejandro Mendez, Director of the National Museum of Panama; Sr. Luis Barriga, Director of the Museo de Oro in Bogota, Colombia; Dr. Gregorio Hernandez de Alba of Bogota, whose books on the subject are well-known; Dr. Maks Portugal in La Paz, Bolivia; and Sr. Carlo Soldi in Lima, Peru; and others whose counsel and assistance have been helpful in the assembly of this collection.

In the rich valleys of North Coast Peru, the Chimu culture flourished from about A.D. 1300 to 1438, when the Chimu were conquered by the Inca. The Chimu were the descendants of the early Mochica who had been subjugated by the Tiahuanaco. Subsequently they re-emerged. The ruins of their famous city Chan Chan, near modern Trujillo, covers an area of almost eight square miles. They buried their important dead in elaborately woven and embroidered textiles. Affixed to these "mummy bundles" were masks, pectorals, and decorations of gold such as these examples.

77-8. MASK—GOLD—CHIMU—AREA OF CHAN CHAN—
W. 24 cm. (9½"), Wt. 68.4 grams

This funerary mask is of cold-hammered gold with the design in repoussé. The nose is superimposed. Unfortunately the cinnabar with which is was partly pigmented was lost in cleaning. (See also color frontispiece)

77-9. PECTORAL—GOLD—CHIMU—AREA OF CHAN CHAN—
W. 50.7 cm. (20⅜"), Wt. 107.32 grams

This pectoral, like No. 77-8, is cold-hammered gold with the design in repoussé. There are also cutouts. The design shows a line of pelicans, the "CY" pattern, and, in the center, the god. (See also color frontispiece)

77-10. NECKLACE—GOLD—OAXACA—Avg. H. 6.2 cm. (2½")

These seven heads of the king vulture—the Coxcacuatli—with pendant bells, were originally joined together through the loops on their reverse sides to form a necklace. Its exact provenance is not known, but we do know the general area in which it was found. It is in the Mixtec style, and its intricate workmanship is as spectacular as any found at Monte Alban by Dr. Alfonso Caso in the famous Tomb VII. Each head is superimposed upon a small plaque which suggests gold wire. However, S. K. Lothrop, foremost authority on pre-Columbian metallurgy, states that this type of work was accomplished by modeling the whole in wax and then casting in a continuous flow of metal. Ex. Coll. William Spratling, Taxco.

77-11. CHISEL—GOLD—QUIMBAYA—L. 13.4 cm. (5¼"),
Wt. 69 grams

This chisel was probably used as a ceremonial replica of the utility chisel which was ordinarily made of copper or bronze. It is interesting to note that duplicates of many of the ordinary work-day utensils, tools, and instruments were also made in gold for religious purposes. It is believed that the gold pieces were used to invoke or propitiate the gods for their assistance in daily pursuits. Ex. Coll. Reinhardt Kling Bauer, Bogota.

77-12. BEAKER—GOLD—CHIMU—H. 14.6 cm. (5¾"),
Wt. 81.5 grams

Of 22-23 karat quality, this cup was found at a depth of 7 meters in the ruins of the fortress city of Chan Chan, near Trujillo, Peru. It is of double construction, with an air space between the two layers on the same principle as the modern thermos glass. The design is in repoussé. Ex. Coll. Nicholas Gessler, Lima.

77-13. DISK—GOLD—CALIMA—D. 12.1 cm. (4¾"), Wt. 49 grams

This disk was probably used as an earring. It has three lines of points towards the border. Found in the Calima Valley of Colombia.

77-14. DISK—GOLD—CAUCA—D. 14 cm. (5½"), Wt. 49.5 grams

This disk with two holes has a line of points in repoussé around the border. It was probably worn as a pectoral. Cauca Valley, Colombia.

77-15. DISK—GOLD—CAUCA—D. 14 cm. (5½"), Wt. 82 grams

This plate has four holes in a rectangular line with repoussé points around its border. It was found in the Cauca Valley, Colombia.

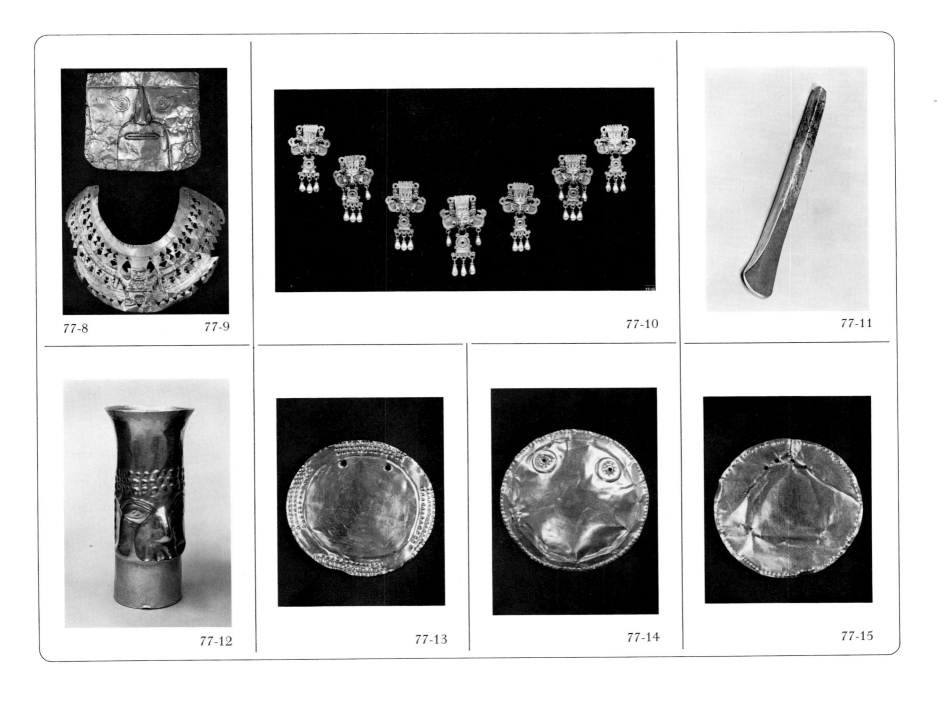

77-8

77-9

77-10

77-11

77-12

77-13

77-14

77-15

77-16. DISK—GOLD—CAUCA—D. 13.6 cm. (5⅜″),
Wt. 42.5 grams

This plain plate has four holes and was evidently suspended as a pectoral. It was found near Restrepo in the Valley of Cauca. Ex. Coll. Fernando Restrepo Velez, Colombia.

77-17. PLAQUE—GOLD—VERAGUAS—D. 15.5 cm. (6¼″),
Wt. 85 grams

This pectoral, with two holes, is adorned with three cone-shaped projections in repoussé and has two lines of points around the border. Ex. Coll. Dr. Alejandro Mendez, Panama.

77-18. PLAQUE—GOLD—VERAGUAS—D. 13 cm. (5⅛″),
Wt. 54 grams

This pectoral, with two holes, is adorned with three cone-shaped projections in repoussé, and has two lines of points around the border. Ex. Coll. Dr. Alejandro Mendez, Panama.

77-19. PLAQUE—GOLD—ANTIOGIA—D. 17 cm. (6¾″),
Wt. 85.5 grams

This pectoral, with two holes, is adorned with ten cone-shaped projections, adornment in the center, and three lines of points. Found in the State of Antioga, Colombia.

77-20. PLAQUE—GOLD—VERAGUAS—D. 21 cm. (8¼″),
Wt. 121 grams

This handsome pectoral, with two holes, is adorned with four large cone-shaped projections, four stylized human face masks, and two lines of points around the border. Ex. Coll. Alejandro Mendez, Panama.

77-21. ANTHROPOMORPHIC HEAD—GOLD, FEATHERS, AND ALPACA HAIR—ICA—H. 16.8 cm. (6⅝″),
Wt. Gold 31.2 grams

This head can be dated as approximately 1300-1400 by other objects found with it. It was found in a burial in the Ica Valley, Peru.

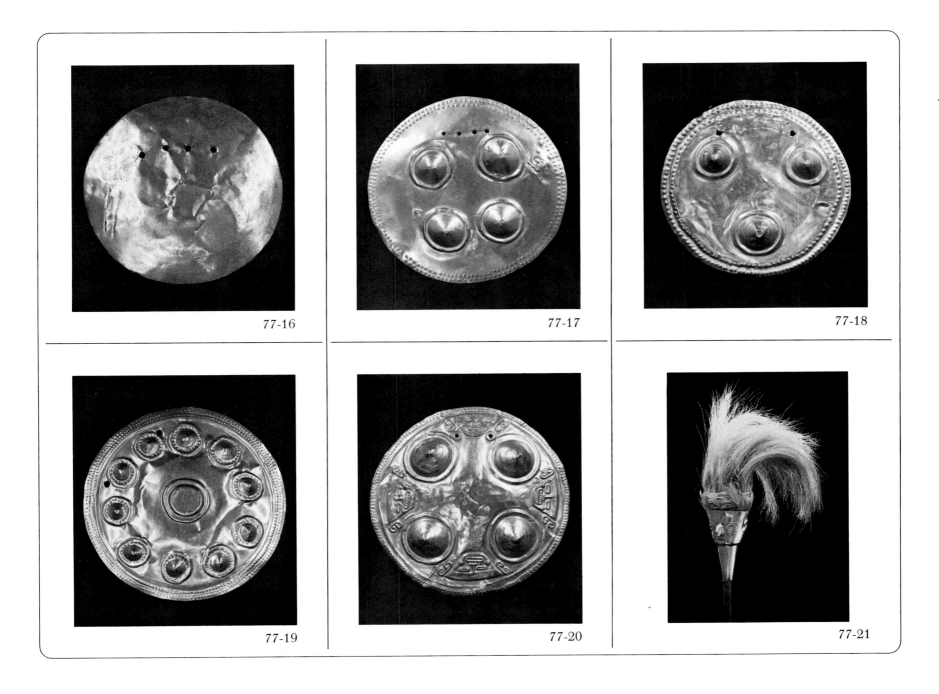

77-16

77-17

77-18

77-19

77-20

77-21

77-22. PENDANT—GOLD—CAUCA—H. 3.5 cm. (1⅜″), Wt. 12.5 grams

This *cire perdue* anthropomorphic figure is fashioned to be hung as a pendant. Cauca Valley, Colombia.

77-23. PENDANT—GOLD AND OBSIDIAN—CHIRIQUI— H. 2.5 cm. (1″), Wt. 10 grams

This amusing gold and obsidian pendant has the obsidian worked in a tooth-like shape, and the gold is in the form of the face of an owl. Costa Rica.

77-24. ANTHROPOMORPHIC FIGURE—GOLD—COCLE— H. 2.5 cm. (1″), Wt. 7.5 grams

This cast figure is of extremely fine workmanship and can be best appreciated under a glass. The figure has two heads with a single body and is intricately decorated. Panama.

77-25. SEGMENT OF NECKLACE—GOLD—VERAGUAS— L. 2.5 cm. (1″), Wt. 7.5 grams

This piece appears to have been threaded as part of a necklace. Inasmuch as it was found alone, however, it may have been worn suspended with nothing additional. It depicts two small lizards on a decorated log. Ex. Coll. Alejandro Mendez, Panama.

77-26. BELL FIGURE—GOLD—CHIRIQUI—D. 2.5 cm. (1″), Wt. 12.5 grams

This anthropomorphic figure is *cire perdue* cast. It is in the form of a bell and depicts a human figure with a double-headed snake in his mouth. Costa Rica.

77-27. BELL FIGURE—GOLD—CHIRIQUI—H. 4 cm. (1⅝″), Wt. 31.5 grams

This anthropomorphic figure is *cire perdue* cast. It is in the form of a bell and depicts a human figure playing a musical instrument. It was found near Puerto Armuelles, Costa Rica.

77-22

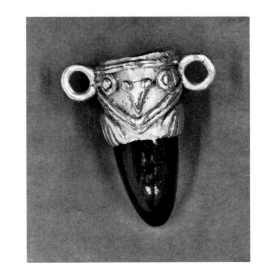

77-23

77-24

77-25

77-26

77-27

77-28. NOSE PIECE—GOLD—VERAGUAS—D. 2 cm. (¾″), Wt. 10 grams

This nose piece was initially cast and then hammered to form the bottom flange. Note how well its style goes with No. 29, which is Chiriqui. Panama.

77-29. FIGURE OF DEITY—GOLD—CHIRIQUI— W. 7 cm. (2¾″), Wt. 29 grams

This *cire perdue* casting has two wings soldered to its head-dress, and decorations in points of gold adorn its head and legs. This lively figure was found in northern Panama.

77-30. ANTHROPOMORPHIC FIGURE—GOLD—SINU— H. 7 cm. (2¾″), Wt. 44 grams

The extremities of this figure are very stylized as are the decorations of the head. *Sinu* goldwork, although simple in design, is quite heavy. Colombia.

77-31. SKELETON—GOLD—COCLE—H. 6 cm. (2⅜″), Wt. 23 grams

This stylized skeleton form is most unusual. It appears grace-ful, modern, and extremely sophisticated. Ex. Coll. Alejandro Mendez, Panama.

77-32. ANTHROPOMORPHIC FIGURE—GOLD—TIERRA DENTRO—H. 4 cm. (1½″), Wt. 26 grams

This figure is elaborately decorated and is an involved *cire perdue* casting. Colombia.

77-33. NOSE PIECE—GOLD—CARCHI—W. 6 cm. (2⅜″), Wt. 9 grams

This nose piece is intricately hammered, and the ends of it are soldered coiled gold wire. It was found in northern Ecuador.

77-90. EFFIGY STAFF—GOLD—CALIMA—L. 27.5 cm. (10⅞″), Wt. 33.8 grams

These pins of cast gold were used to fasten the robes of the nobility. The detail shown here is the pin's finial, a figure of a male wearing a headdress and carrying an object in each hand.

151

77-28

77-29

77-30

77-90

77-31

77-32

77-33

77-34. ANTHROPOMORPHIC FIGURE—GOLD—CHIRIQUI—
H. 6 cm. (2⅜″), Wt. 31.5 grams

This cast and soldered figure holds two emblems of command in his hands. It was found near Puerto Amuelles, Costa Rica.

77-35. ZOOMORPHIC FIGURE—GOLD—COCLE—D. 3 cm. (1¼″), Wt. 13.9 grams

This figure is cast, and the circle is affixed by soldering. It has four holes and evidently was worn. Panama.

77-36. ZOOMORPHIC BELL—GOLD—VERAGUAS— D. 4.5 cm. (1¾″), Wt. 17.5 grams

This bell appears to be in the shape of a bat standing in a circular arc—his tail? Ex. Coll. Dr. Alejandro Mendez, Panama.

77-37. ZOOMORPHIC FIGURE—GOLD—CHIRIQUI—
D. 6 cm. (2⅜″), Wt. 35 grams

This figure, which appears to be a monkey, has a decorated tail which forms a circle that terminates in the head of a serpent. It is a casting subsequently decorated. Costa Rica or Panama.

77-38. FIGURE OF A DEITY—GOLD—LA GUAIRA—
H. 5.5 cm. (2⅛″), Wt. 36 grams

The relationship of this piece to realistic Quimbaya figures is evident in the treatment of the body. However, the elaborate and stylized rendering of head and headdress are of unique complexity. Venezuela.

77-39. BAT GOD—GOLD—CHIRIQUI—H. 7 cm. (2¾″), Wt. 76 grams

This elaborately cast and decorated Bat God figure has the feline head; snakes emanate from his mouth, but he wears a tail. *¿Quien sabe?* Costa Rica.

77-34

77-35

77-36

77-37

77-38

77-39

77-40. FINIAL—GOLD—COCLE—W. 6 cm. (2⅜″), Wt. 15.5 grams

This parrot form still contains part of the original clay of the *cire perdue* process by which it was cast. The holes, with which he was attached as a finial to a wood staff by nails, are visible. Panama.

77-41. HAMMERED NECKLACE—GOLD—POPAYAN—

D. 19.5 cm. (7¾″), Wt. 37.5 grams

This necklace was found in a burial in the Popayan region of Colombia with some skeletal remains. The litomorphic necklace was still in position. It was evidently more or less in the form of a leaf and twig design, which has been partially crushed. About thirty of the original tiny gold nails, which formerly fastened it as a gold covering on wood, were recovered. These original nails were used in the restoration. Colombia.

77-42. REPTILOID FIGURE—GOLD—QUIMBAYA—

L. 3.5 cm. (1⅜″), Wt. 10 grams

This figure appears to be a decorated lizard. Ex. Coll. Reinhardt Kling Bauer, Bogota.

77-43. ZOOMORPHIC FIGURE—GOLD—QUIMBAYA—

L. 3.2 cm. (1¼″), Wt. 16.6 grams

This figure appears to be a decorated fantastic animal. Ex. Coll. Reinhardt Kling Bauer, Bogota.

77-44. ZOOMORPHIC FIGURE—GOLD—CAUCA—

L. 6 cm. (2⅜″), Wt. 19.5 grams

This is the *cire perdue* casting of a jaguar. It was found by the James A. Ford Expedition in the valley to the north of Cauca and is a variant of the style formerly included with Quimbaya. Colombia.

77-45. ZOOMORPHIC FIGURE—GOLD—VERAGUAS—

L. 5.5 cm. (2⅛″), Wt. 24.5 grams

This is a double-headed *cire perdue* casting of a fantastic animal. It was found in Panama.

77-40

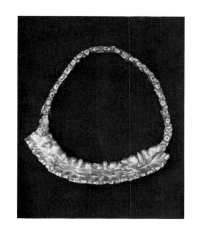

77-41

77-42

77-43

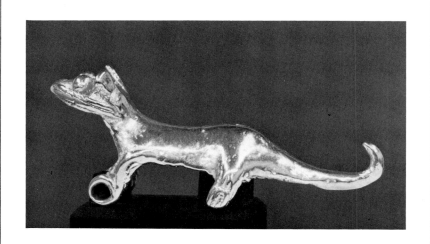

77-44

77-45

77-46. ZOOMORPHIC FIGURE—GOLD—VERAGUAS—

L. 7 cm. (2¾"), Wt. 40 grams

This figure has two heads. It is finely decorated and has holes which enabled it to be worn as a pendant. Ex. Coll. Alejandro Mendez, Panama.

77-47. FROG—GOLD—NICOYA—L. 6 cm. (2⅜"), Wt. 31.5 grams

This frog is well formed and is decorated. Its legs are in the customary conventionalized form with splayed feet. It was found in Costa Rica.

77-48. BRACELET—GOLD—VERAGUAS—D. 7 cm. (2¾"),

Wt. 63 grams

This bracelet contains two bells which are very well articulated. The segments are decorated. Panama.

77-49. CASCABELS—GOLD—TOLTEC—various sizes,

Wt. 38.5 grams

These seven bells (cascabels) were found in the State of Nayarit, Mexico, and were all probably pendant together. Gold finds are extremely rare in this area.

77-50. EAGLE—GOLD—CHIRIQUI—W. 5 cm. (2"), Wt. 12 grams

This is a miniature of its general type. The head is unusually finely decorated. Panama.

77-51. ZOOMORPHIC FIGURE—GOLD—CHIRIQUI—

W. 5.5 cm. (2⅛"), Wt. 21 grams

This winged piece is uniquely stylized. It is cast, soldered, and decorated. Panama.

77-46

77-47

77-48

77-49

77-50

77-51

77-52. EAGLE BELL—GOLD—MIXTEC—H. 4 cm. (1⅝″),
Wt. 22 grams

This bell, in the form of an eagle pectoral, is very finely decorated in the head, wings, and tail. The bell is articulated. It was found near Monte Alban in the State of Oaxaca, Mexico. It is very similar in style to the Chiriqui of Costa Rica.

77-53. DOUBLE EAGLE PECTORAL—GOLD—CHIRIQUI—
W. 4.5 cm. (1¾″), Wt. 13.5 grams

This complicated casting is decorated and represents twin eagle forms. It was found at Puerto Amuelles, Costa Rica.

77-54. DOUBLE PELICAN PECTORAL—GOLD—ESMERALDAS
—W. 8.5 cm. (3⅜″), Wt. 39.5 grams

This pectoral appears to represent two pelicans and seems to be several castings soldered together rather crudely. Northern Ecuador.

77-55. EAGLE PECTORAL—GOLD—VERAGUAS—
W. 12 cm. (4¾″), Wt. 99 grams

This eagle pectoral is decorated on its head, neck, and feet. Ex. Coll. Dr. Alejandro Mendez, Panama.

77-56. DOUBLE EAGLE PECTORAL—GOLD—VERAGUAS—
W. 13 cm. (5⅛″), Wt. 88.5 grams

This single pectoral with two heads is of an inferior quality gold. Ex. Coll. Dr. Alejandro Mendez, Panama.

77-57. EAGLE PECTORAL—GOLD—VERAGUAS—
W. 13.5 cm. (5¼″), Wt. 130 grams

This eagle form, upon analysis, assays absolutely pure gold. It is well-decorated on the neck, wings, and head, and is an extremely fine example. Panama.

77-52

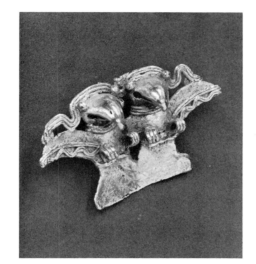

77-53

77-54

77-55

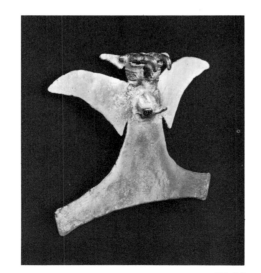

77-56

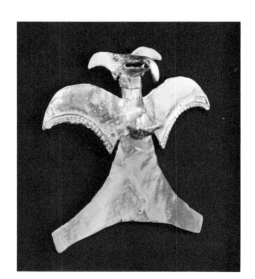

77-57

159

77-58. ZOOMORPHIC FIGURE—GOLD LEAF PLATED—
COCLE—L. 91.5 cm. (36″), Wt. 55.5 grams

This tiger is an example of the plating which these people did by lining a mold with gold leaf and then pouring in the hot copper. It is a lively figure in the position of attack with the mouth open, the ears extended forward, and poised to spring.

77-59. EAGLE PECTORAL—DIPPED GOLD PLATED—
VERAGUAS—H. 10 cm. (4″), Wt. 95 grams

This eagle is a casting on which was applied a different technique. The casting was dipped in a heavy bath of molten gold.

77-60. PELICAN PECTORAL—TUMBAGA—VERAGUAS—
W. 7 cm. (2¾″), Wt. 22.5 grams

This pelican is an example of very low quality gold. The metal contains a great deal of copper and silver.

77-61. ANTHROPOMORPHIC FIGURE—MERCURY-GOLD
PLATED—QUIMBAYA—H. 7.5 cm. (3″), Wt. 36.5 grams

This figure, with a bird head, shows an interesting technique. This piece was first coated with a mixture of mercury and powdered gold. Heat then drew off the mercury and deposited the gold.

77-62. FROG—MISE EN COULEUR—NICOYA—L. 4.5 cm. (1¾″),
Wt. 12 grams

This frog, with extended eyes and conventional splayed feet, is an alloy of gold and copper on which acid has been used to eat away the surface copper and float the gold.

77-63. ICHTHYOMORPHIC FIGURE—TUMBAGA—VERA-
GUAS—H. 7.5 cm. (3″), Wt. 27 grams

This figure is in the form of a beautifully stylized sea horse. It is another example of tumbaga of superior quality.

77-58

77-59

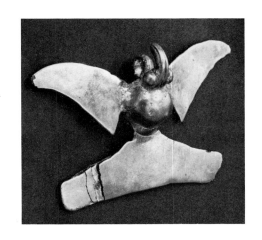

77-60

77-61

77-62

77-63

77-64 and **77-65. EAR RODS—JADE AND GOLD—COCLE—**

L. 23.7 and 24.1 cm. (9⅜″ and 9½″)

These rods, found at Venado Beach, were worn suspended through the ear lobes.

77-66. MASK—JADE—PYROXENE—TOLTEC STYLE—

H. 32.2 cm. (12¾″), W. 34.6 cm. (13⅝″)

This beauty was one of our most exciting finds. A barefoot Indian, working in the vicinity of the practically undisturbed small pyramids in the hills near Tepoztlan in the valley of Mexico, uncovered it. The ear and nose plugs, of course, were gone. Stone masks of this type originated with the Teotihaucan peoples, and the style spread, with variations. Drawings show them being worn on the chest with ceremonial attire. This mask has aroused controversy as to its authenticity. It is one of the largest extant. Experts in Mexico and the United States have expressed different opinions on it. However, we know where and how we found it, and we believe it not to be "falso."

77-67. CELT—MOTTLED JADEITE—GUANACASTE—

H. 21.5 cm. (8½″)

This ax god in the form of a human figure was found at Santa Cruz, Guanacaste, Costa Rica.

77-68. CELT—GREYISH GREEN JADEITE—NICOYA PENINSULA—H. 11.8 cm. (4⅝″)

This ax god represents a man. The bead earrings, found with the figure, possibly belong to it.

77-69. PENDANT—JADE—SPINACH CHLOROMELINITE—GUAPILES—L. 12.2 cm. (4¾″)

These so-called winged pendants have been found in Mexico, Costa Rica, Panama, northern Colombia, and in the West Indies. Occasionally, the body and head of a bat were carved in the center, indicating that the whole group symbolizes a bat with extended wings.

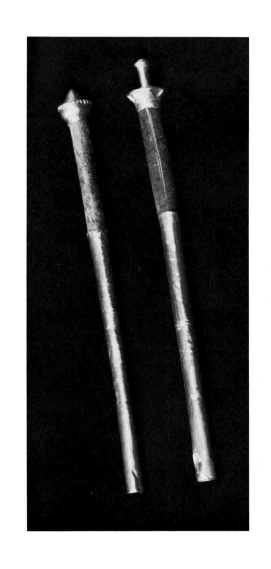

77-64 and 77-65

77-66

77-67

77-68

77-69

77-70. CELT—BLUEISH GREEN JADEITE—NICOYA
PENINSULA—H. 11.1 cm. (4⅜″)

This ax god is an extremely stylized anthropomorphic figure.

77-71. PENDANT—SISKIN GREEN JADEITE—GUAPILES—
H. 9.7 cm. (3¾″)

This is an example of string sawing, a technique typical of this locality. To free the arms and legs, first a hole was drilled. Then a string, impregnated with an abrasive, was inserted, and a slot was cut by sawing.

77-72. CELT—WHITISH JADEITE, FLECKED BLUE—
GUANACASTE—H. 14.2 cm. (5⅝″)

This human effigy is a pendant.

77-73. CELT—METAMORPHIZED QUARTZ—ZAPOTEC—
L. 15.7 cm. (6¼″)

This ax was found at Monte Alban, Oaxaca, in II Period strata. It was probably ceremonial rather than utilitarian.

77-74. CELT—GREEN JADEITE—GUANACASTE—
H. 10.4 cm. (4″)

This ax god pendant represents a bird.

77-75. PENDANT—GREEN JADEITE—NICOYA PENINSULA
—H. 5.3 cm. (2⅛″)

This pendant, of superior quality, represents a bird.

77-70

77-71

77-72

77-73

77-74

77-75

77-76. PECTORAL—JADE, CELADON AND WHITE JADEITE —MIXTEC—H. 8.1 cm. (3¼″)

This three-quarter profile sculpture was found at Monte Alban.

77-78. PIERCER—GREEN JADEITE—OLMEC—L. 21.6 cm. (8½″)

This object of beautiful quality jade was found in Puebla, Mexico. It appears to be a tongue or ear piercer.

77-79. BEAD NECKLACE—GREEN JADEITE BEADS— MIXTEC—L. 25.3 cm. (10″)

These beads were found in Chiapas, Mexico.

77-80. PENDANT—GREEN JADEITE—MIXTEC— H. 2.9 cm. (1⅛″)

This represents the carved head of a man.

77-81. AMULET—JADE, DARK GREEN NEPHRITE— GUERRERO—H. 6 cm. (2⅜″)

This small jade figure was found in the solidly packed earth inside a funerary urn. It appears to be in the Guerrero style and was probably a trade piece.

77-82. PLAQUE—GREYISH DIOPSIDE JADEITE— ZAPOTEC(?)—H. 15.2 cm. (6″)

A seated god is wearing an elaborate head dress, ear studs, and a pectoral. Other figures surround him. Jades of this type passed in trade or as tribute over great distances, and there is positive evidence that some were inherited for many generations before they were buried with their owners.

77-76

77-78

77-79

77-80

77-81

77-82

167

77-83. PLAQUE—GREEN JADEITE—ZAPOTEC(?)—
H. 10 cm. (4″)

This carved plaque depicts a standing figure.

77-84. PLAQUE—MOTTLED GREEN JADEITE—TOTONAC(?)
—H. 7.9 cm. (3⅛″)

This plaque was found in the Vera Cruz area. It represents a human head in the open jaws of a serpent. It appears to be Late Classic Style.

77-85. PROFILE—CARVED SHELL WITH JADE INLAY—
MAYA—L. 7.9 cm. (3⅛″)

There are very few examples of these shell bas-relief profiles of Maya personages extant. This one was found on the Island of Jaina, off the Yucatan Peninsula. Incised glyphs, the plumed quetzal bird over the human head, and considerable detail are not badly eroded. Ear ornaments, necklace, and decoration are small cabachon cut inlays of jade. The asymmetrical pose is typical of Late Classic Style.

77-86 and 77-87. EAR DISKS—GREEN JADE—TOLTEC—
W. 8.2 cm. (3¼″)

These ear disks were found in the Valley of Mexico and are not a pair.

77-88. ANTHROPOMORPHIC FIGURE—JADE—DARK
NEPHRITE—OLMEC—H. 15.1 cm. (6″)

This standing figure of a man is strongly muscled, and a small breech cloth is the only clothing indicated. This is of the so-called "baby face" type, characteristic of Olmec sculpture. Frontal deformation of the skull is evident. Found in Puebla.

77-83

77-84

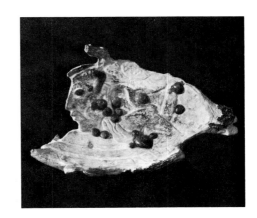

77-85

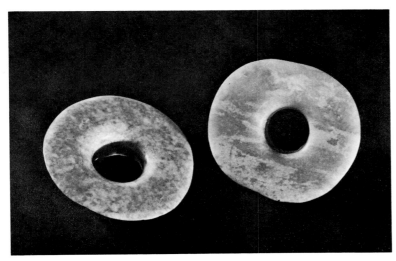

77-86 and 77-87

77-88

77-89. ZOOMORPHIC FIGURE—SERPENTINE—WILLIAMSITE —OLMEC—H. 16.4 cm. (6½")

This figure with a human body and the jaguar face appears to be in the fetal position. This position appears occasionally. No. 79, page 000, shows a very similar Tiahuanaco figure found near Cuzco. This was found in a burial in Campeche.

77-91. MOSAIC MASK—TURQUOISE, LAPIS LAZULI, AND SHELL—CHIAPAS AREA—H. 6.1 cm. (2⅜")

The Spaniards greatly admired the mosaic work of these people, hence their present rarity. From its provenance this small example is probably Toltec-Maya. It represents a human mask. This technique was used to cover human skulls, idols, masks, helmets, knife handles, etc. Mosaic pieces found in archaeological excavations are generally difficult or impossible for restoration. This piece has no restoration.

77-89

77-91

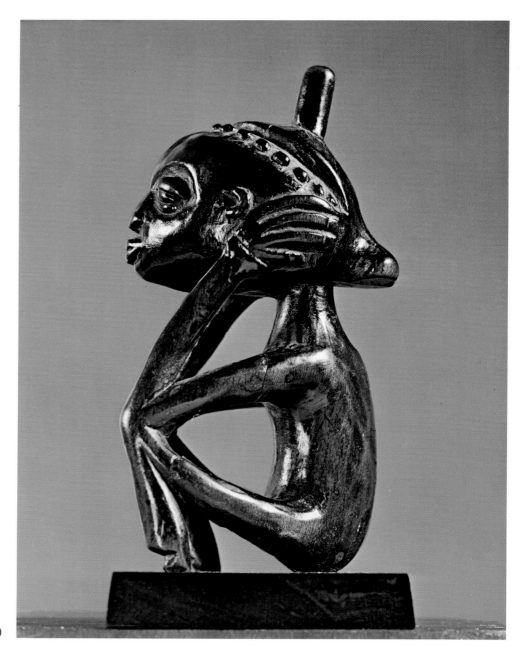

BENA LULUA FETISH (CATALOG NO. 286)

SECTION VI. NEGRO AFRICA

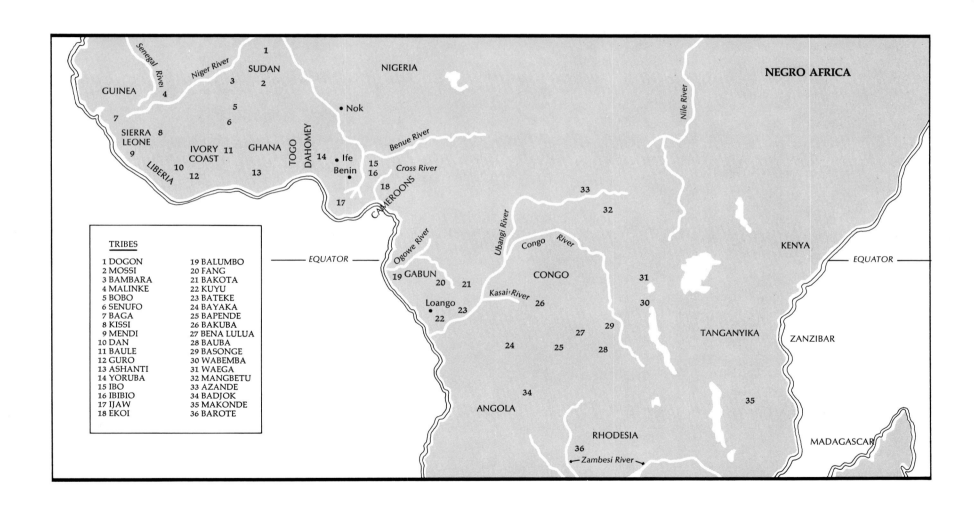

NEGRO AFRICA

TRIBES

1 DOGON
2 MOSSI
3 BAMBARA
4 MALINKE
5 BOBO
6 SENUFO
7 BAGA
8 KISSI
9 MENDI
10 DAN
11 BAULE
12 GURO
13 ASHANTI
14 YORUBA
15 IBO
16 IBIBIO
17 IJAW
18 EKOI

19 BALUMBO
20 FANG
21 BAKOTA
22 KUYU
23 BATEKE
24 BAYAKA
25 BAPENDE
26 BAKUBA
27 BENA LULUA
28 BAUBA
29 BASONGE
30 WABEMBA
31 WAEGA
32 MANGBETU
33 AZANDE
34 BADJOK
35 MAKONDE
36 BAROTE

The word Africa was originally applied to the country in the immediate neighborhood of the Phoenician city, Carthage, that part of the continent first known to the Romans, and the name was subsequently extended generally with their increasing knowledge. If ancient Egypt and Ethiopia be excluded, the story of Africa known to us is largely a record of the doings of its Asiatic and European conquerors and colonizers. Mediterranean Africa was first colonized by the Phoenicians, and, as early at 631 B.C., the Greeks founded important cities from Cyrene to Alexandria (See 2nd Map). Then Roman control succeeded the fall of Carthage in 146 B.C. Six hundred years later, the barbarian Vandals briefly established suzerainty. Then in the VII century A.D. an Arab host from the east, following the new faith of Mohammed, conquered all of North Africa from the Red Sea to the Atlantic. Through the following centuries, North Africa has been primarily Islamic.

In the XV century, Europe coveted. Prince Henry, "The Navigator," who never went to sea, inspired the series of explorations which resulted in Portuguese sovereignty over large areas of Africa's coast lands. Lucrative trade, including slaves and alluvial gold, attracted English, Spanish, Dutch, French, and Danish adventurers. For centuries the white man's slave trade and pillage exploited, but never developed, this great continent. As Jonathan Swift versified:

> Geographers in Afric maps,
> With savage pictures fill their gaps,
> And o'er uninhabitable downs
> Place elephants for want of towns.

During the last quarter of the XIX century, European interest in Africa again revived, and the continent became the theatre of European imperialism. Africa's map was transformed as lines of partition, often through trackless wilderness, were drawn to mark out the "possessions" of the European powers. Neither Herodotus' tales, which hazard ancient African explorations, nor the motion picture, which has popularized "blackbirding," nor the writings of Speke, Burton, Livingston, Baker, Stanley, or their successors dissipate Africa's feral opacities.

We have already discussed Egypt and North Africa as this area has closer ties with the Mediterranean world than with the rest of its own continent. In prehistoric North Africa lived the proto-Egyptians, a sub-sized, brownish people. They were not Semitic, but repeated waves of invaders over the centuries assimilated them. These Hamitic people, who were also not Negroid, only dark skinned, but with the fine features and soft, not wooly hair, and the Pygmy Negrillos, a distinct race, found both in the north and to the south, had been pushed out of Central Africa by the Negroes. They have left their record in the highly artistic cave rock drawings, megalithic monuments, menhirs, and dolmens of Ethiopia, the Sudan, southern Libya, and Algeria. The Negro locus is Equatorial Africa. But actually the boundary line between "Negro Africa" and "White Africa" must be provisional.

"The Dark Continent" lacks the most important evidence of historical consciousness—writing. So, as its own history is primarily one of internal migrations, it presents a unique historical passivity. Obviously, though, this early habitat of homo sapiens shared all of man's turbulent phylogeny. States grew up and disappeared. As early as 1491, the king of the Congo was baptized and recognized by the Roman Pope. Nineteenth-century European explorers were astonished to find his ruined churches. Here wars were fought, and the peace made and broken, dynasties prospered and withered, but this history is unrecorded.

It is pertinent that you know of Africa's progressive climatic change. Areas in North Africa, now desert, were comparatively recently lush, the habitat of the antelope and the lion as attested to by the ancient steles and drawings of the hunting in the Mediterranean area. As recently as 1922, the black-maned Barbary lion roamed Morocco. But Africa is rapidly drying. The encroachment of the Sahara during the last three centuries has absorbed 390,000 square miles, and in Kenya the desert advances against the primeval forest at the rate of six miles a year.

Around the turn of this century, the term "primitive art" brought to mind the sculpture of Africa, almost to the exclusion of all else. The work of Oceania and the Americas was known to scholars and specialists, but the enthusiasm of artists, which had been communicated to the public, was largely for African art. And, due to the accidents of colonizing history, African art meant work from only two areas: the figures and masks of the Ivory Coast, refined and delicately carved; and the wood and metal grave guardians—Bakota and Fang of the Gabun region, simpler and more directly religious in concept, bolder and more abstract in style, many of them weathered so that they appeared centuries old. Today our knowledge of African art has expanded both geographically and chronologically. The fanciful datings have given way to the realistic knowledge that Africa is mostly a country of wood, and a couple of hundred years of climate and termites spell a short life expectancy for wood carvings. So, what remains is at most only a few hundred years old but is founded upon ancient tradition and lore.

Strangely enough, at the same time that the Matisses, the Picassos, the Braques, the Derains, and the avant-garde of Paris discovered African Negro sculpture, they revealed to Africa itself that it had an art. Art was a European notion, unknown in these tribal societies, where there is no exact translation for the word "beauty." But the African obviously has a keen sense of beauty. Call them artists, craftsmen, or what you will, always remember that some artisans are more perceptive and skillful than others, and neither age nor provenance may ever, in any culture, be used as an index of excellence. Terror of the unknown is probably the most important motivating force of Africa's ritual sculpture, and, as the intermediary between man and the supernatural forces, it is better compared

to religious art of the Middle Ages than to present-day "creative art."

The men's leagues, both secret and open, were the cornerstone of Equatorial Africa's social structure. Masks functioned in these societies for all ritual occasions—initiation, circumcision, puberty, fertility, feast, dance, and burial. The female predominates in ancestor figures, probably a carryover from an original matriarchal culture. The African lives closely with his amulets and reserves the right to thrash or destroy these fetishes if they fail him. They were only created to communicate with spirits and daemons, to propitiate or outwit them.

Style ranges from extreme naturalism to extreme formalism, from crudity to great refinement. The law of frontality is inexorable. One rarely sees the typical Negro face. Animism led to the use of ritual masks and fetishes. This is the belief that all objects in the world have consciousness and personality. These spirits may include the dead, leading to ancestor worship, or they may be general, non-personalized spirits or daemons.

The ivories and bronzes of Benin, the gold pieces of the Baule, the Ashanti gold weights, the fantastic fertility and ancestor figures, the grotesque, but at times very beautiful, society and tribal masks have only interested Europe since 1905. But so-called "primitive art" has admittedly vastly influenced modern art. Examples follow.

257. BAULE PENDANT—GOLD—IVORY COAST—W. 8.6 cm. (3⅜")

This golden mask in the form of a stylized ram's head, traditionally a symbol of creation, owes its originality to the human face between the horns. The ram frequently appears as a cult animal.

258. BAULE PORTRAIT FIGURE—WOOD—IVORY COAST—H. 42.1 cm. (16½")

Baule art is a secular art. Portrait types are the most usual style of sculptural subject as in this example of a young girl. There is a small piece of gold on her necklace, and the cloth is original. Ex. Coll. Le Duc.

259. BAULE PENDANT—GOLD—IVORY COAST—H. 7.6 cm. (3")

This golden pendant, decorated with a horned human mask, was originally purchased at the Hotel Drouot, Paris, auction of the André Derain Collection.

260. BAGA COMB—CARVED WOOD—GUINEA—L. 35.2 cm. (13⅞")

This votive comb, decorated by a mask and carved figure, was part of the treasury found at N'Goran-Yad-Kro by the French Punitive Expedition of 1910.

261. SENUFO CEREMONIAL MASK—WOOD—SUDAN—H. 32.5 cm. (12¾")

This mask, with typical scarifications and horns, has thin slit eyes.

262. DAN CEREMONIAL MASK—WOOD—LIBERIA—H. 22.9 cm. (9")

The profile of this mask, which forms a continuous line, is noteworthy. Fine patina.

263. DAN CEREMONIAL MASK—WOOD—LIBERIA—H. 21.9 cm. (8⅝")

The ovoid concave face of this mask shows metal teeth and a moustache made of raffia. Poro secret society.

264. TWO MAKONDE FIGURINES—EBONY—TANGANYIKA—H. 17.6 cm. (6⅞")

These figurines are contemporary. Certain natives, whom we have seen in this area, display surprising facility in carving them in hardwood, using both their hands and feet with dexterity.

257

258

259

260

261

262

263

264

265. EKOI CEREMONIAL MASK—WOOD—CAMEROONS—H. 34.1 cm. (13½″)

This mask shows Negro naturalism. The Ekoi live on the Cross River. They betray signs of a skull cult and at one time covered their masks with human skin.

266. IBO INITIATION MASK—WOOD, MONOCHROME—NIGERIA—H. 29.3 cm. (11½″)

Of grim aspect, this mask shows tattoo design and a complicated hair dress. The initiation ceremonies were held to "graduate" the boys into the role of adult males in tribal life.

267. IBO GHOST MASK—WOOD, KAOLIN, PAINT—NIGERIA— H. 34.6 cm. (13½″)

White represents death to these people. On the kaolin-white, paint is applied for the design of scarification and tattoo.

268. BAPENDE SOCIETY MASK—WOOD, MONOCHROME— CONGO—H. 25.1 cm. (13⅞″)

Brutal Cubism and strong planes characterize this mask of the type used in circumcision ceremonies for the boys of the tribe.

269. YORUBA CARVED TUSK—IVORY—NIGERIA—L. 39.8 cm. (15¾″)

The Yoruba sculptors became pre-eminent. This carving depicts scenes from the daily life, as well as westerners. Attributed to Arowogon of Osi, whose work is represented in the British Museum.

270A. TWO ASHANTI GOLD WEIGHTS—BRONZE—GHANA (GOLD COAST)—L. (a) 8.9 cm. (3½″), (b) 8.7 cm. (3⅜″)

These small castings of anthropomorphic and zoomorphic figures were allegedly used as gold weights and functioned as money. (a) Fantastic animal, (b) male nude astride. *Cire perdue.*

270B. THREE ASHANTI GOLD WEIGHTS—BRONZE—GHANA (GOLD COAST)—H. (a) 6.4 cm. (2½″), (b) 8.3 cm. (3¼″), (c) 5.9 cm. (2¼″)

(a) Seated warrior, (b) male and female figures, (c) warrior on horseback. Of unpretentious, short, anecdotal character. *Cire perdue.*

270C. TWO ASHANTI GOLD WEIGHTS—BRONZE—GHANA (GOLD COAST)—L. (a) 10.4 cm. (4¼″), H. (b) 10 cm. (4″)

(a) Wounded antelope, (b) kneeling native aiming a gun; show this art at its stylistically freest. *Cire perdue.*

265

266

267

268

269

270A(b)

270B(c)

270A(a)

270B(b)

270B(a)

270C(b)

270C(a)

272. BAKOTA FUNERARY FIGURE—COPPER, BRASS, WOOD—
GABON—H. 61.1 cm. (24⅛″)

Funerary figures of this type, fastened to reliquary baskets in which the treasured skulls of revered ancestors were placed, were kept in family shrines by the Bakota. Perhaps such stylized heads as this, with features in full face and coiffure in profile, suggested to Picasso his early Cubist portraits.

273. ASHANTI MASK—GOLD—GHANA (GOLD COAST)—H.
7.6 cm. (3″)

This gold fetish in the form of a human face is a particularly fine ornament of its type.

274. BAULE AMULET—GOLD—IVORY COAST—H. 9.1 cm.
(3⅝″)

In the form of a bull's head, this was evidently a fetish for the Negro's most valuable possession, his cattle. Embellished with close hatching.

275. BAMBARA ANTELOPE HEADPIECE—WOOD—SUDAN—
H. 45.8 cm. (18″)

Chi Wara, legendary antelope spirit of the Bambara of the French Sudan, was associated with agriculture and a bountiful harvest. Each spring, dances celebrated the fertility of the earth and the helpfulness of *Chi Wara*. This headpiece was worn during these vernal rites.

276. GURO INITIATION MASK—WOOD, MONOCHROME—
IVORY COAST—H. 32.2 cm. (12¾″)

This mask, with two birds atop it, was used for initiation ceremonies into tribal secret society. It is carved with unusual delicacy.

277. GURO SOCIETY MASK—WOOD, GESSO UMBER—IVORY
COAST—H. 36.9 cm. (14½″)

These masks were used in the secret society dances of Gore and Guie.

278. GURO TOTEM MASK—WOOD, PAINT, GESSO—IVORY
COAST—H. 36.4 cm. (14⅜″)

Surmounting this mask is a pair of totem birds. Brilliant patina.

279. GURO FETISH MASK—WOOD, GESSO—IVORY COAST—
H. 40.3 cm. (15⅞″)

The figure of a seated white man, with dog, on this mask was possibly meant to exorcise the foreign devil, the slave trader.

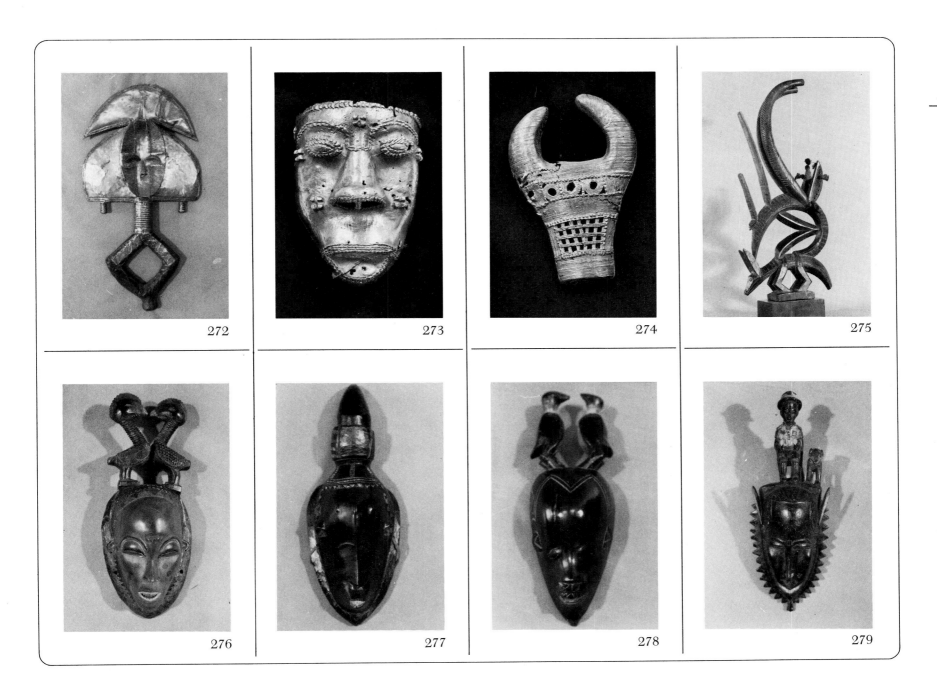

272

273

274

275

276

277

278

279

280. YORUBA CEREMONIAL AX—BRASS—NIGERIA—L. 56.2 cm. (22⅛″)

Carved and engraved, this weapon was probably used for presentation.

281. BENIN STATUE—BRONZE—NIGERIA—XVI-XVII CENTURY—H. 22.6 cm. (9″)

This effigy of a warrior in the round shows full armor and an unusual tiara-shaped headdress. It was found at the Palace of the Benin Kings (Obas) by Dr. R. B. Allman, C.M.G., principal medical officer at the time of the Benin Punitive Expedition in 1897, according to Dr. Allman's letter extant. The powerful Kingdom of Benin, like the Ashanti and Dahomeyans, had a well-organized government and possessed a culture rare in Africa and an unenviable notoriety for human sacrifices and slavery.

282. BAKOTA THROWING KNIFE—WROUGHT IRON AND BRASS—GABON—L. 41.6 cm. (16⅜″)

In the form of a cock, including the spur, this throwing knife shows a superb, stylized form.

283. EKOI PIPE BOWL—ARGILLITE—CAMEROONS—H. 19.1 cm. (7½″)

This anthropomorphic squatting figure is sharply modeled. It was used as a pipebowl.

284. BAYAKA FETISH MASK—WOOD, POLYCHROME—CONGO—H. 44.4 cm. (17½″)

The heart-shaped face with the carved fetish animal beneath is peculiar to this tribe.

285. BAKUBA CEREMONIAL MASK—WOOD, POLYCHROME, CLOTH, COWRY SHELLS—CONGO—H. 42.6 cm. (16¾″)

A practically identical mask, attributed to Bena Lulua, appears in Werner Schmalenbach's *African Art*, New York: the Macmillan Co., 1954, pl. 128, p. 143.

286. BENA LULUA FETISH—EBONY—CONGO—H. 10.6 cm. (4⅛″)

This beautifully carved amulet against Africa's endemic dysentary is in the typical squatting position. (See also color plate, this section.)

280

281

282

283

284

285

286

DETAIL OF THE *Triumph of Darius*, ATTRIBUTED TO THE MASTER OF THE JARVES CASSONE (CATALOG NO. 298)

SECTION VII. AND TO TODAY

In Section II we left Europe drowning in the great tide of barbarism which engulfed the civilized world shortly before A.D. 500. Then came the thousand years of *Christendom*, which might be called, rather, the Age of the Barbarian Invaders, following the thousand years of Rome. After the Huns, after the Germanic tribes, came the Arabs, the Norsemen, the Magyars, the Turks, and the Bulgars. The barbarians strangled civilization; Christianity preserved it. Very clearly it drew the teeth of paganism. But during these Dark Ages, save in the refuge of monastaries, men's knowledge, laboriously accumulated for thousands of years, was lost. Even the ability to read disappeared. Art reverted to a primitive style. The ornamentation of the barbarians was closer to prehistory than to the perfection of Greco-Roman culture. Constantinople temporarily became Rome's heir, and for hundreds of years Byzantium became the commercial center of a world which had forgotten trade. This temporary custodian of surviving culture supplied its glittering art of Oriental ornamentation. Most important, Syrian-Armenian Byzantine architects solved the problem of the true pendentive, which had eluded Rome, and realized the artistic possibilities of the spherical dome. Witness Hagia Sophia. But incongruously, this turbulent period marked the hatching of the great European nations.

We cannot here detail the spawning of the modern states, which occurred during this period. Had not Clovis, the Frankish leader, defeated the Alamanni, Gaul might have become Germany; possibly Burgundy, had he not driven back the Burgundians; possibly Catalonia, had he not beaten the Visigoths. Actually as a result of his triumphs, she became France. And Charlemagne (ca. 800) constructed a genuine empire, only for it to be divided under the Treaty of Verdun (843) into embryonic *France*, *Germany*, and *Italy*. Languages, as well as countries, were at this time irremediably, distinctly sundered.

In Section II we indicated the *Arabs*' African and Asiatic conquests in the epoch after Mohammed. These Arabs—sometimes called Moors or Saracens—gained a beachhead in European Spain (Semitic word). But the infidels were evicted by the Cid (1050), who personally symbolizes this whole epic struggle which laid the foundations for the Spanish royal house of Castile. However, the entire vast Arab empire was too loosely knit to survive, merely a kaleidoscopic amalgam of territories. The *Turks*, who originated in Central Asia, captured Bagdad (1055), and ultimately Asia Minor became a Turkish country. Turks were Mussulmans, the enemy of the Church, whom she attacked during the almost two centuries of the *Crusades* for the deliverance of the Holy Places. The Arabs, more adaptive than creative, after their containment became the middlemen between east and west and revealed to the west the treasures of the east. They gave birth to a mixed art style in which both Persian arches and Byzantine vaulting had their place. The richness of its decorative invention achieved astonishing triumphs.

Meanwhile the piratical Norsemen, who called themselves Vikings, from the Scandinavian Peninsula terrorized western Europe. Around the year 800, Norsemen were primitive savages with an art confined to personal ornaments and decorated weapons. They possessed a runic form of writing but had no early literature. These sailor-Scandinavians were triple scourges—Norwegians, Swedes, and Danes. The *Norwegians* ravaged Ireland, Scotland, the islands of the White Sea, and even touched the American continent (999). The *Swedes* turned toward the Slavic lands. They began with the Baltic coast. One of their tribes—Russians—gave their name to the whole country. They founded a powerful principality reaching to the Upper Dnieper and the Black Sea and actually threatened Constantinople. The *Danes*, who unlike their two neighbors cared neither for discoveries nor trade, were the most devastating blight. They established footholds in the Low Countries and, sailing up the rivers, repeatedly burned Rouen, Paris, Bordeaux, Saintes, Hamburg, Lisbon, and many other places. They massacred the clergy of Nantes. A fresh wave of Danes beat back the Anglo-Saxons and won all of England. Their Canute was recognized as England's king (980). England escaped the Danish yoke only to fall into the hands of the Frenchified Norsemen from Normandy. William the Conqueror beat the Saxons at the Battle of Hastings (1066). The old home of the Britons was henceforth to be an Anglo-Norman kingdom, and William's companions-in-arms became the ancestors of future English barons.

Before the Norsemen had ceased ravaging western Europe, a new set of nomads swept westward: the Bulgars and the Hungarians. These savages derived from the Huns. The *Bulgars* settled in present Bulgaria (660). Within three hundred years they had carved out a considerable realm. They converted to Greek Christianity and adopted a Slavic language. Civilization quickly softened them, and, shorn of their savage vitality, they were reduced (970), but they left their name on the Balkans. Then followed the *Hungarians*, who called themselves Magyars. The indigenous Slovenes, Serbs, Croats, Slovaks, Czechs, Moravians, Pomeranians, and Poles were fully occupied, as ever, fighting each other, and the Hungarian hordes, with only the skills of horsemanship, archery, and pillage, had no difficulty in seizing the Danube Plain. For a short time—some fifty years—they devastated their neighbors: Venetia, the Po Valley, Saxony, Lorraine, Basle, Tuscany, and to the Bosphorus. Then the Hungarians, too, learned to plough; civilization and religion overtook them, and they entered the concert of Christian European nations. The Pope anointed their King-Saint Stephen and blessed his diadem, which has remained the sacred symbol of the Magyar nation. From this rich fermentation of assimilated marauders came the major spawning of Europe's geographical errors—today's chauvinistic, xenophobic nations.

During this night of barbarism, towns fell into ruins, fields ran to seed, roads were no longer kept in repair. The rule of violence made all trade impossible. Each great estate was a closed economy, self-supporting, isolated. A *Feudal* regime ensued. One prevalent fear held that the year 1000 would witness the end of the world. Before the year 1000 the Emperor of the Holy Roman Empire, an anachronism, neither holy, Roman, nor an empire, a pale reflection of ancient Rome, but the dominant European political entity, was forced by the papacy to drink his cup of humiliation (1077). We shall not go into the relentless, endless quarrels of the frequently impious popes against the emperors as the church sought temporal power. For this period, the church became the arbiter of the whole Christian community.

The opening of the XIII century marked the awakening of the west. Sovereigns broke free of the pontifical leading-strings. England and France openly defied the papacy. In cruel, fanatical retaliation, the tribunals of the Inquisition began to operate. Passions waxed hot as Christian men embarked upon an orgy of killing in the name of Christ. Most apocalyptic! The rediscovery of the idea of the state spelled the decline of the papacy. In 1215 England's King John signed the Magna Carta, really guaranteeing feudal privilege, not the liberty of the subject, but leading to the establishment of Parlia-

ment. France established a system of primogeniture for its crown, and the secret of continuity became the secret of France's future greatness. Chaotic, unstable, modern France has forgotten this.

So, in the XIV century, on stage was assembled the main cast of characters, the major nations of the world as we know them today. Western man's geographical and ethnological ecology had at least temporarily coalesced. Possibly gunpowder was the cause. The Chinese and Indians had long used gunpowder only for the manufacture of fireworks. In European hands (ca. 1330) the dangerous mixture became a fighting weapon. It eliminated for all time the menace of the nomad. Never again would there be another Attila, another Genghis Khan, another Tamerlane. Europe, with its fire-spitting jaws, was to control the destinies of this planet.

During the next two hundred years the Spanish, Portuguese, French, English, Dutch, and Swedes would discover and dismember the lands of the New World. But in the Americas would evolve a most un-European harmony and homogeneity of man. After the colonizing most of these people would sever Europe's umbilical cord. The great nations of the Americas would emerge, and their citizens would enjoy and build upon their Old World heritage. And in Europe the endless strife would continue. There would be the ascendancy of Italy, then of Spain. There would be the centuries of France and then the Anglo-Saxon centuries. There would be the bloody religious Reformation and a Counter-Reformation. There would be the birth of the Low Countries, the French Revolution, and invariably the wars. But all of this remains ancillary to the pattern which then was molded.

Another five hundred years, and the XIX century fathered the Industrial Revolution into our XX century of technology. And now the Religion of Progress proselytes. Can it supplant all others? Even discounting the formal dogma of the churches, does man not require the consoling buttress of some faith? Walt Whitman remarked that one blade of grass can confute a thousand atheists. Our world, far from becoming united, continues to disintegrate. The Building of Babel at the United Nations continues to receive scores of new, competitive, mutually suspicious, jealous states, irremediably hostile to each other. Remember that pacifist illusion wrought havoc in Hellas.

The Pandora's box of technical progress which today has been opened contained, besides the gifts of creature comforts and conveniences, over-amusement and leisure, some very disconcerting baubles. Demographic and scientific knowledge misdirected inevitably will lead to mutual slaughter. Politicians and venal labor leaders have captured us. They attempt to repeal the natural laws although it is obvious that only through compliance with these laws can the boons of agricultural and mechanical development avoid overproduction, recurrent crises, and poverty. Private enterprise is dying, and with it will die all human liberties. Improved medicine, paradoxically, lowers the quality of the race. By keeping alive the weak and the diseased at a time when wars eliminate the fit, the processes of natural selection have been counteracted. The perfecting of credit systems has merely loosed upon the world the curse of inflation. A re-examination of man's history confirms that now all of the necessary ingredients are compounded for parlous prospects. In the twelve thousand years since the Neolithic Age, man has discovered so much about the world and so little about himself.

The salient difference between man and animal is that man consciously bequeaths his experiences to succeeding generations. The evolution of man's art, in juxtaposition with his history, appears to afford a certain political and economic prescience. There now follows the very briefest chronicle of this, eschewing the pretentious jargon currently the fashion when discussing art.

Architecture was indeed Mistress Art during the Middle Ages. Following the death of Roman material civilization, the people of central and western Europe, recently barbaric, were at first unequal to the task of creating their requisite buildings, and, due to their recently acquired Christianity, churches. Naturally they returned to Roman and Byzantine inspiration. The resultant initially crude style, which includes regional differences and various types arrived at during the XI to early XII centuries, is termed *Romanesque*. National boundaries were then non-existent, and the first master builders were indubitably itinerant monks along "pilgrimage road," who transmitted tradition in an attempt to empirically build impressive churches, as richly decorated as possible. Their technical skills were incomplete, and their materials were crude. Romanesque walls were universally heavy; the round arch was employed; columns were stocky; and the churches followed the Roman basilican ground plan. Late Romanesque churches were spanned by barrel and groined vaults. Lavish color decoration was found on simple surfaces. The general effect was of intense, vigorous emotion, incomplete achievement, and sombre gloom.

The sculpture was plastic, archaic ornament incorporated into the building, adapting itself to its architectural panel. Thus, the story of Christ was represented in a dramatic style, easy for simple folk to apprehend. The struggle of men against monsters and the powers of hell, horrible grotesqueries largely drawn from the bestiaries, were calculated to terrorize the non-repentant sinner. Witness: Romanesque buildings at Caen, Toulouse, Compostella, Parma, Venice, Durham, Hildesheim, and Spires.

During the late XII century there was a metamorphosis throughout Europe as if, almost suddenly, latent decorative imagination and technical skill had reached maturity. The most important development of Romanesque architecture had been continual experiment with vaulting. Completely stone-vaulted churches were necessitated by frequent disastrous fires in the old wooden-roofed buildings. Now the controlling problem was counteracting the thrust or outward pressure of high, heavy nave vaults. The solution came with the adoption of the pointed arch of the Saracens. It was introduced into France by her Norman knights, returned from the Crusades. Most of Italy rejected the style and derisively named it *Gothic*. So most of Italy was to remain dominantly Romanesque into the XIV century, which partially explains Italy's early Renaissance as she largely skipped a Gothic Period.

However, from the middle of the XII century in the Ile de France, utilizing ribbed vaulting, pointed arches, and flying buttresses—the salient features of Gothic architecture—churches soared with an upward thrust of nave, tower, and steeple. This vertical style became a skyward leap, lost in a luminous fairyland of stained glass. It was a style of extravagance, an integral part of which was rich carving and a profusion of statuary, illustrative of Biblical texts. Gothic appeared to seek the assurances of salvation in a time of perpetual petty wars and of the *Crusades*. This is further exemplified by colorful, Scriptural paintings, sumptuous altar pieces, reliquaries, and the fruition of illuminated manuscripts. The Gothic style spread to Cologne, to Toledo and Burgos, to Canterbury and Ulm and Prague. Stone lost its coldness and solidity; sculpture became freer. The Angel of Rheims learned to smile, the Sainte Chapelle grew to a wonder of lace. Mont-Saint-Michel tapered to a soaring delicacy.

The Italian *Renaissance* may be considered as from the Trecento—starting early XIV century, the time of Dante and Giotto, and spanning the period to Titian's death in 1576. Italy was broker and banker between east and west, and her riches, including the papacy's "wealth of all Christendom," fostered the revival of learning, scientific observation, and the arts. Interest in the humanities deliberately led her artists to the classical forms of antiquity. Architecture, too, effectively borrowed from this past. New techniques evolved. Murals were executed in fresco. New grandeurs of conception were introduced. Perspective, unknown to the ancients, became the artists' chief interest.

We cannot here enumerate all of the names of the inspired masters whose brilliance illuminated the glory of this Renaissance. With popes, princes, and merchant princes as patrons in local centers, a plethora of fine artists developed. The XV century in Italy produced such giants as Masaccio and Piero della Francesca. The painter was largely emancipated from the bondage of religious subject matter, and suddenly paintings were peopled with living individuals. And ever the list of genius grew! For example, it is recorded that in the year 1503, Leonardo—the Universal Man—Michelangelo, Perugino and his young pupil Raphael, Botticelli, di Credi, Fra Bartolemmeo, Filippino Lippi, and del Sarto were all working in Florence. Mantegna, the Bellinis, Vecchio, Giorgione, and Titian were painting jewels for the crown of Venice. Bramante was designing St. Peter's. Slightly earlier were Donatello, whose great statues were the application of classical canons with freedom of expression, and Ghiberti, whose sculptured bronze doors for the Baptistry were executed in the detailed style of the goldsmith. There was a host of greats!

But what alchemy in mortals creates any Age of Pericles? Why in Italy, during an age of individualism, when powerful princes—Medici, Pitti, Visconti, Malatesta, Montefeltro, Este—controlled political life and waged merciless, internecine wars did this fabulous array of talent appear for a period of over two hundred years? And why did this manifestation as suddenly suffer eclipse? Bernard Berenson declared that Italy has produced no great painter since 1600.

By mid XV century, beyond the frontiers of Italy, the Gothic tradition was exhausted. The English Gothic style was buried under a complex system of decorative ribs, while in France Gothic lost its spontaneity and became confused in a riot of flamboyance. Then, the Northern Renaissance dawned. The Lowlands, with a newly surgent middle class, enjoyed sufficient prosperity to erect great belfry-towers, market buildings, and guild halls. It was there that easel-painting (ca. 1420) made its appearance with the brothers Van Eyck—a form of art more intimate than fresco, less sketchy than illumination. The new technique followed the discovery of oil used as a drying, mixing, and glazing medium which imparted to painting a freshness, transparency, and durability previously unknown. Why are these great masters of this period, as Rogier Van der Weyden, Hugo van der Goes, and Memling, called Flemish primitives? Do art historians recognize in their great works the naïveté of a Grandma Moses or traces of Africa or Oceania? We cannot. The fame of these artists of the Low Countries spread over Europe, and Flemish painters themselves became articles of export.

In the XVI century, Spain reaped the economic harvest of her discoveries in the New World—gold and silver. And, through the person of Charles V and his son Phillip II, Spain curiously inherited several of the most important countries and the political ascendancy of Europe. Art follows wealth and power. The Escorial, Phillip II's huge new palace near Madrid, received an influx of Flemish and Venetian painters. Out of this milieu of imported artists arose the transcendant, independent Cretan, El Greco, who developed a manner suffused with wholly Spanish mysticism. Spain became one of the last countries to relinquish the medieval formula for her Renaissance. Her churches were adorned with paintings in the Italianate and Flemish traditions. In Italy, now scarcely more than a Spanish colony, still lived the incomparables—Michelangelo, Titian, Cellini, and a host of other greats to apotheosize. In Venice there were Tintoretto and Veronese. We are particularly attracted to sequential bronze statuary, especially the sensuous suavity of Bologna. The grandiose classical architecture of Palladio now originated. A development during this period was a complex intellectual revolt against the ordered rationality of the Italian High Renaissance termed *Mannerism*, a misnomer.

The Netherlands was now also just another Spanish province. Flemish art proceeded from the surrealistic inventions of Hieronymus Bosch to the father of popular art, Breughel the Elder. In Germany, the Reformation had tempered the Renaissance. Dürer, painter, engraver, and woodcut maker, must be regarded as the eminent

German artist. Contemporary with him were Altdorfer's rich innovations, Cranach the Elder's witty, fertile originalities, and Grunewald, creator of the Isenheim altarpiece's mystical significance. Holbein the Younger expatriated to Switzerland and later to England to become the most sought after portraitist of this age. Ironically France, destined to be the leader of the Modern Movement in painting, was quite sterile. Even French chateaux were still built upon modified Italianate lines. French sovereigns continued to summon Italian masters to Fontainebleau. The late XVI century in Italy saw the advent of *Baroque* asymmetrical tendencies and melodramatic lighting in painting. This voluptuous development also permeated architecture and is still to be seen in some of Europe's most venerated buildings.

So at the start of the XVII century with the fervor of the Italian Renaissance growing cold, the Baroque tendency prevailed. Bernini expressed Baroque in architecture and in sculpture. Spain embraced this new style which El Greco had foreshadowed. Three men of Seville—ascetic Zurbaran, sentimental Murillo, and elegant, austere Velasquez—carried Spanish painting to new distinction. From Iberian sources the Baroque style was carried to the New World. (The familiar Northern Baroque which established in southern Germany and Austria was almost 100 years later.) From the Netherlands vital Rubens, the epitome of the Baroque, and his follower Van Dyck exerted their influence throughout Europe. Some thirty years later would arise the great school of Dutch painting immortalized by the virtuosity and versatility of Rembrandt, genius of chiaroscuro. Franz Hals is of prime importance for his individual and group portraits. Finally we find juxtaposed the gemütlich portraits, landscapes, and studies by Vermeer, de Hooch, Cuyp, Van Goyen, and Ruisdael in contrast to the lusty, rowdy tavern sets of Brouwer and Steen.

Later in the XVII century the power of Spain waned, and France assumed the mantle of European dominance, and art reverted to another Classic Age. The Sun King, Louis XIV, built Versailles, and it reflects his passion for order and symmetry. His influence is mirrored in the cold, intellectual quality of his court painters and their strivings for perfection. Learned Poussin and naïve Lorrain who spent most of their maturity in Italy were the bellwethers who now bequeathed their legacy of formalism. But with Louis' death in 1715 French art abandoned itself to frothy elegance, adapted to the sophistication and gaiety of the court. France was the greatest power in the world for this period. Her language held the widest currency. She was the most thickly populated and most productive of all European nations. Contrary to popular misconception, France was in no decline during the last years of the monarchy. Her art, though, now suffered the decadence of the gay, decorative *Rococo* mutation. This change is more marked in the sculpture of Pajou and Houdon than in the charmingly executed paintings of Watteau, Boucher, and Fragonard. The substantiality of Chardin's still-lifes are in marked contrast to his contemporaries, as are the naturalistic pastel portraits of La Tour. After Louis XV came "the deluge."

Again the world was convulsed. The Revolution, the Terror, and Napoleon Bonaparte. The child of the revolutionary political, social, industrial, and scientific permutations in art is the *Modern Movement*, which was initiated some one hundred and fifty years ago. The ideal of the Academy was superseded by a new ideal. In place of the essentially religious works of the medieval, the richness of the Renaissance, the intricacies of the Baroque and Rococo, a new realism and individuality became popular. At first, in an age of reason and scientific discovery, the problem of light was to absorb the painter. He turned to landscape to study in natural color the effect of sunlight and shadow. The invention of photography produced radical changes in the theory of vision and in the problems of reality. The public museum, a comparatively recent innovation, permitted the artist to study the works of the great masters. There was opportunity for eclecticism. Revolutionary techniques, the basic new laws of composition, the objective representation of actual things, the "significance of form" and how it may be achieved by pure color; all of these things were learned, together with a new taste for subject matter.

It finally became evident that the battle of modern painting was to be waged between the visual world of fact and the abstract, subjective, inner world of passion and intuition. Previously painting had become definitely pictorial, a recording of historic fact, either in portraiture or as an illustration of important events. But the commercial possibilities of steel engraving and photography relieved the artist of external pressures and provided greater opportunity for personal expression. There appeared in the hundred years which followed the French Revolution more styles of individual painting than had been known in the preceding five thousand years of the history of art.

A curious contribution to art emanates from Spain. She has never produced galaxies of art luminaries. But, from Spain has come the bridge spanning the turn of three of these past four centuries. We have already observed that the idiom of El Greco, after his death, actuated the Baroque advent into the XVII century. Starting the XIX century a revolutionary as great as El Greco—that giant, Francisco Goya, painter and etcher—profoundly affected art from his day until the present, especially in the divergent flux of Impressionism and Expressionism. And later we shall see that, ushering in the XX century, another Spaniard, Picasso, became the most influential evocator of our times.

However, art and artists for these past one hundred and fifty years, with the sole important exception of Picasso's ambivalence, may be fundamentally separated into three categories—*Neoclassicism*, *Romanticism*, and *Realism*, all existing coevally. At the inception of the XIX century in France the aesthetic aspirations of the "ancien regime," Napoleonic imperialism, and academic conservatism were satisfied by the antique revival. This was the *Neoclassicism* of David's compositions and Ingres' clarity of line.

The origins of the *Romantic* Movement are to be found in the late XVIII century culture of Germany and England from whence it moved to France. Here, in the XIX century, it found expression in Delacroix's passion and hot glamor and Géricault's short-lived, socially conscious enthusiasms.

The direct antithesis of the then prevalent classical theory was the *Realistic* faction which settled in the small village of *Barbizon* to paint nature as they saw her. The later nominal head of this group was Theodore Rousseau. It included Millet, more of a figure painter, and Daubigny, interested in plein-air principles anticipating the Impressionists. Aloof Corot's discreet masses and planes were independent of the "school" as were rebel Courbet's materialistic works. Also apart was gifted Daumier, the penetrating, satirical, graphic artist, whose caricatures have obscured his relationship to the development of modern French painting. That fine British landscapist, John Constable, exhibited in the Paris Salon in 1824. He was to exert tremendous influence upon the Barbizon School and upon Delacroix,

the Romanticist's spontaneity, so let us visit England to observe her development.

In retrospect, during the Renaissance, England's art had been primarily foreign court importation—Holbein, Lely, Van Dyck, and others collected by ill-fated Charles I. After the Restoration (1688) indigenous artists awoke. Starting with Hogarth, an elegant, graceful school of portraiture arose. Of course Hogarth is better known for his satirical moralities. The British School developed to dull Sir Joshua Reynolds, founder of the Royal Academy, and Gainsborough's and Lawrence's epitomes of period portrait painting. Then during the XIX century as portraiture in the British Isles declined, the art of landscape painting waxed stronger. Constable represents a full step forward in the modern development of landscape art. You have heard of his immediate influence upon the French. Turner, the distinguished landscapist, was to be of later influence upon the French Impressionists. Monet and Pissarro acknowledged their debt to his symbolic abstractions of the forces of nature—"the inner meaning of a given idea"--following their London visit to the master. The visionary work of that solitary, mystic figure, William Blake, stands conspicuous in Romanticism.

The early contributions of the United States were largely of her expatriates during Colonial days—West, Copley, and Stuart. Later, after the Civil War, her local art was to be lifted out of the provincial stage by a succession of remarkable painters, some of whom also became expatriates: Homer, Innes, Whistler, Eakins, Ryder, La Farge, Sargent, and Cassatt.

And now in the 1860s we return to France and the ferment of another revolution in art—*Impressionism*. This movement was to spread throughout the world during the following thirty years, and the works of most "founders" of modern art have had roots in some phase of it. Manet's explorations of new modes of vision made him the precursor of Impressionism, but he would not embrace its loose technique.

Impressionist painting, which originally centered in Paris, may be described as somewhat formless, flecked, color divisions with an emphasis on the transitory and ephemeral as opposed to that which is linear and clearly silhouetted. The artists moved their easels outdoors and exhibited a pseudo-scientific interest in light and color phenomena. Their attitude was more empirical and lyrical than theoretical. Often the play of light so dissolved the forms that reflections appear as authentic as actual objects. A rainbow palette was used purely, brightly, and in separate strokes. However, of this period and also appreciated today are the still-lifes and flower paintings of Fantin-Latour, who remained an independent.

In its time, Impressionism was met by public ridicule, and most of its exponents faced dire poverty. Curious, when its sheer, sensuous delight is so prized today. Its major disciples were Monet, Pissarro, Sisley, and Morisot. And Renoir bathed the painting of the Impressionists with his superb "pagan hedonism," achieved by the rotation of warm and cool tones. Degas' exquisite paintings and sculptures mark another culmination of the Impressionist movement.

Then followed a turning away from the Impressionist naturalism. This reaction is awkwardly called *Post-Impressionism*. Illustrious Cezanne, pupil of Pissarro, rejected the Impressionistic formula with its lack of solidity and design. He concentrated on form and controlled space arrangement using color in successive planes to project form from the canvas to achieve permanence of effect. Seurat and Signac broke up the spectrum into a series of dots and spots of pure color known as *Pointillism*. Van Gogh, revealing through violent vibrations of color his own inner conflict, and Gauguin, opening up the exotic possibilities of the South Seas, pointed toward the following more intuitive and emotive art of the Fauves and the Expressionists. Simultaneous with the Neoclassicism of Cezanne and Seurat and the Romanticism of Van Gogh and Gauguin, was Toulouse-Lautrec, whose caustic cynicism on painting, poster, and lithograph immortalized the brothels and cafes of Montmartre.

At long last we reach our XX century. But before continuing with painters and paintings, we ask what has happened to sculpture in our times. Alas our tactile sense remains unassuaged by its continued comparative non-acceptance. From antiquity, sculpture has been a part of our heritage. Now it is in decline. In the century past Rodin stands pre-eminent. The charming bronzes of Daumier, Renoir, and Degas were not the medium of their prime expression. During our times, sculpture has followed the classical traditionalism of Lehmbruck, Maillol, Lachaise, Bourdelle, Sintenis, Despiau, and Epstein; the Cubist abstraction of Lipchitz, Brancusi, Mestrovic, Archipenko, and Laurens; and the Expressionist experiments of Barlach, Moore,

Modigliani, Giacometti, Marini, Arp; and Calder's mobiles. But the tendencies are diverse and chaotic. The incongruity of the welding torch seems incompatible in the artist's studio.

To return to painting, in the first decade of this century the term Fauvism was derisively derived from the French word *fauve* or wild beast to describe the work of a group of painters including Matisse, Braque, Vlaminck, Derain, Dufy, and Rouault. They continued the trend of the Post-Impressionists but tried to impart motion to their canvases through dynamic color. However, they always observed compositional and formal limitations. After a very few years the disciples abandoned this mode and reverted to their individual styles.

The first decade also felt the first impact of the most influential artist of our century—Pablo Picasso, that truly protean figure. It was Picasso and Braque who broke up individual form into sharply angular planes, then allowed the separated facets to slip, become transparent, and merge with the background of the painting. This is termed *Cubism*. Leger, with his machine-sharp precision, was the third of the leading Cubists. And there were the systematic geometrics of Gris. However, the first World War shattered the artists' hopes for a scientific world of art. But the chameleon Picasso's virtuosity and brilliance would continue ubiquitous.

And still intellectualism in art continues to run its course during our XX century. Through *Expressionism* the artist tries to destroy external reality and arrive at its "truth" or emotional essence, employing distortion of form, color, and space. Basically Expressionism is emotive and allegedly soul searching, not descriptive or analytical. This movement emerged primarily from Germany and Austria.

There are three basic types of Expressionism. The Bridge formulation, stemming from Van Gogh, African sculpture, and Fauvism, results in distorted but still representational forms. This is the style of Kirchner, Nolde, and Schmidt-Rottluff. The Blue Rider or abstract variety derives more from Gauguin, Delaunay, and folk art and results in rhythmic expression in which form penetrates form and color penetrates color. This is illustrated by Marc, Kandinsky, Klee, and Macke, and, in certain respects, Feininger. The third category is New Objectivity, representational but very intense in mood and clinical in detail. This is exemplified by Dix and Grosz. There are a few independent Expressionists in Germany and Austria, including psychological Kokoschka and the personally emotional symbolism of

Max Beckmann. But outside this geographical area we find Rouault, Soutine, and Edvard Munch; the latter, along with Ensor and Hodler, marks the transition between *Symbolism* and Expressionism.

To list some bellwethers of this era through the nihilistic "non-art" of Arp and Ernst's *Dadaism* and to today would include witty, provocative phases of Duchamp, the Italian *Futurists*, the assymetrical balance of Mondrian's *Purism*, the spatial unreality of de Chirico, the biological imagery of Miro, the psychic experience of Dali, the symbolism and fantasy of Chagall, Redon's poetic imaginativeness, the personal expression of Marin and Davis, and the architectonics of Sheeler, Demuth, O'Keeffe, and Blume. For the "American Scene" there are Wood and Benton, Shahn and Hopper. And among recent *Abstractionists* must be included Pollock, de Kooning, and Motherwell. There is also the validity of the Mexican social-struggle school depicted by Rivera, Siqueiros, Orozco, and Tamayo.

The emphasis on the subjective in the later works of the *Dadaists* and *Surrealists* has led, quite logically, to the extremely sterile abstractions of our time. The Modern Movement established itself in the United States at the celebrated Armory Show in New York (1913) when many of the European radicals were shown. But never for this long century has a semblance of consonance in art been attained.

Can this be the assertion of the undisciplined individual, rejecting the accumulations of the art of centuries for a personal catharsis within his limited experience? It appears that a great many people with nothing to say are now saying it. The study of anatomy and the art of draftsmanship are curiously absent. It is premature, perhaps, to appraise, so we shall forebear. But architecture also, *sans* adornment, might be likened to living and working inside a test tube. Today's painting is open to hoax. Splash and splatter does not satisfy us. Is innovation an end unto itself? We are shaken when Sir Herbert Read solemnly concurred with an artist who declared that he was "interested in force, not aesthetics." André Malraux, articulate and possessed of great erudition, propounded, "Ignorance may partially explain the masses' dislike of modern art, but there is also a vague distaste for something in it which they feel to be betrayal." So continues man's quest for aesthetic expression.

Following the collapse of the Roman Empire in the V century, all Europe suffered the barbarian invasions and for hundreds of years languished in a Dark Age. Finally a renascence of learning and art initiated with wise Charlemagne's Carolingian Empire. A fragmented medieval world that wanted unity found it in the immutability of the Church. So with the inspiration of faith, all arts paid obeisance to church architecture and to its decoration. It evolved from the Carolingian, through the ambivalent, contemplative, and violent Romanesque style, into the soaring Gothic style, and found fruition in the spirit of Renaissance victorious. Here are examples of the decoration from these architectural styles.

293. CAROLINGIAN ARCHITECTURAL FRAGMENT—SAND-STONE—VIII CENTURY—W. 98.4 cm. (38¾″)

Found in Northern France, this weathered stone has within a border carved with an inscription, an intricately interwoven pattern, typical of the period, the second Frankish Dynasty of Charles Martel and Charlemagne. Translation of the inscription by Professor Paul Friedlander, University of California at Los Angeles, "He worked hard so that these works would be done."

294. ROMANESQUE CAPITAL—LIMESTONE—XII CENTURY—W. 29.7 cm. (11¾″)

The Romanesque style may be explained as a salutary encounter between the influx of the Germanic world's then violent forces and the Latin world, whose viable heritage is still with us. Depicted is the agonized human and the bestiary allegory of the Middle Ages. From the Province of Auvergne, France. Vestiges of gilt.

295. GOTHIC CORBEL—WHITE LIMESTONE—XIV CENTURY—H. 30.1 cm. (11⅞″)

The transition to the sharp Gothic style from the blunt Romanesque is evident in this corbel and in No. 297, below. They are from Martignon House in Rozerieulles, Moselle, France. Ex. Coll. De Motte, London.

296. GOTHIC BAS RELIEF—LIMESTONE—XIV CENTURY—H. 66 cm. (26″)

Here are portrayed two saints under arches ornamented with floral spandrels. From France. Ex. Coll. George Gray Barnard, Metropolitan Museum, New York City.

297. GOTHIC CORBEL—WHITE LIMESTONE—XIV CENTURY—H. 30.5 cm. (12″)

This corbel has the same provenance as No. 295, above, and is similar to it.

293

294

295

296

297

298. TRIUMPH OF DARIUS—OIL AND GILT CASSONE
PANEL—MID XV CENTURY—W. 155.2 cm. (61⅛"),
H. 41.5 cm. (16⅜")

The late Bernard Berenson believed the "Triumph of Darius" was executed by a painter close to Domenico Veneziano, probably in his atelier, where with assistants he carried out his master's designs. Berenson has catalogued him as the Master of the Jarves Cassoni. This is of the Florentine School active in the middle of the XV century.

Cassone is the Italian term for chest or coffer, usually a bridal or dower chest, highly ornamented and given prominence. Major artists such as Uccello and Botticelli painted *cassone* panels, and prominent sculptors were called upon to carve elaborate chests. The *cassone* was usually decorated with mythological or historical episodes. It became one of the first means of secular expression in Renaissance art.

Depicted here is a triumphal procession with Darius as a youth in the center. Behind him and a little lower ride his mother, his wife, and two daughters. The influence of Uccello is evident in the fine horses and that of Fra Angelico in the landscape, but the composition is more advanced than in the comparable work of Uccello. The costumes and the landscape show a still Gothic love of detail. It is ever curious to note that these Renaissance painters did not attempt the costumes of antiquity, in this instance V century B.C. Persia. The costumes and trappings are those of the then contemporary 1450 Florence. Similar treatment of the Triumph of Darius may be seen in panels in the Cinughi Collection, Siena, the Crawford Collection, London, and the Landau Collection, Florence. This is framed in the original polychromed wood. (See also color plate detail, this section.)

REFERENCES: B. Berenson, on the Master of the Jarves Cassoni; R. Offner, School of Pesellino (Frick Art Reference Library, May 4, 1928); *Cassoni*, Paul Schubring, Leipzig, 1923. Ex. COLLS. Harold I. Pratt, Wildenstein & Company, New York. REPRODUCED: Wildenstein & Company's *Italian Paintings*, 1947, No. 9; *The Painter as Historian*, November, 1962, p. 45. CITED: E. A. Jewell, *New York Times*, January 19, 1947.

299. RENAISSANCE CHERUBS—MARBLE—EARLY XVII CENTURY—W. 55.7 cm. (21⅞")

Dating from the early XVII century, this charming sculpture of three winged cherub heads shows the initial invasion of Baroque tendency upon the style of the Italic Renaissance. Ex. Coll. Blumka, New York.

298

299

300. SAINT CHRISTOPHER AND CHILD—CARVED FRUIT-WOOD—SPANISH—XVII CENTURY—H. 41.7 cm. (16¾")

This carving was brought from Spain by a Captain Gajardo in the early XVII century and remained at his family *fundo* in Chimbarongo, Chile, until we acquired it there. It was in extremely bad condition which necessitated the stripping of the original gesso, gilt, and polychrome decoration.

301. HORSE—BRONZE—GIOVANNI BOLOGNA—ITALY—XVI CENTURY—H. 15.9 cm. (6¼")

This bronze was executed by Giovanni Bologna after a drawing by Leonardo da Vinci now in the Windsor Royal Library Collection, No. 12341. Ex. Colls. Prince Trivulzio, Milan, and Adolph Loewi, Los Angeles.

302. GROUP OF THE PRESENTATION—CARVED OAK—ANTWERP—XVI CENTURY—H. 43.2 cm. (17")

This Renaissance carving depicts the robed figure of the Virgin, wearing a species of hennin and supporting the nude Child, who rests upon an altar hung with drapery. The High Priest, with the lineaments of the Emperor Maximilian, is preparing to perform the circumcision. Ex. Coll. Antocolsky, Paris.

303. BAS RELIEF—CARVED MARBLE—FRENCH—XVIII CENTURY—W. 67.6 cm. (26⅝")

This Neoclassic bas relief represents Aurora in her chariot surrounded by Vulcan, Mars, Apollo, Cupid, and the river gods.

300

301

302

303

304. BUST OF ETHIOPIAN—BRONZE AND MARBLE—DATING UNKNOWN—H. 41.8 cm. (16½″)

Acquired in England, this bronze head has been attributed as Roman and the marble base as dating from the Renaissance. It may, however, be a later work in these styles. "Married pieces" are not too unusual.

305. THE NUDE—BRONZE—PABLO PICASSO—1945—INITIALED—H. 29.5 cm. (11⅝″)

This work, illustrated in D. H. Kahnweiler, *The Sculptures of Picasso*, London: R. Phillips, 1949, pl. 215, and called "The Nude," although clothed, is reminiscent of our ancient archaic bronze figurines. Founders Mark, C. Valsvani—5/10.

306. LA FAUNESSE DEBOUT—BRONZE—AUGUSTE RODIN—1884—SIGNED—H. 71.2 cm. (28″)

"The Standing Faun" was purchased through the late Curt Valentine, directly from the Musée Rodin, Paris, while on exhibition in this country in the 1954 Rodin exhibition, which toured many of our leading museums. Published, *Auguste Rodin*, London: Phaidon Publishers, Inc., pl. 33. Despite its name, the figure seems to be leaping.

307. LE CHAR—BRONZE—GEORGES BRAQUE—1935—INITIALLED—W. 26.4 cm. (10⅜″)

"The Chariot" is initialed "G.B." and is marked "3/6" with the founder's mark. Illustrated, Stanislas Fumet, *Sculptures de Braque*, Paris: Braun et Cie., 1951, p. 9 as "Io." A pencil sketch of the subject in *Verve*, Vol. VIII, Nos. 31 and 32. Ex. Coll. M. Knoedler.

308. JOCKEY ON HORSE—BRONZE—EDGAR H. DEGAS—1893—SIGNED—L. 32.2 cm. (12¼″)

This bronze is described in an article in *Jours de France*, November 19, 1956, titled "Degas Perdo et Retrouve." It is one of the bronzes lost during his lifetime and found after his death in 1917 at a caster's in Paris. Illustrated: John Rewald, "Degas XIV-XV," *Art News*, 1955; *Jours de France*, November, 1956. Signed. Founders Mark, A. A. Herraru.

304

305

306

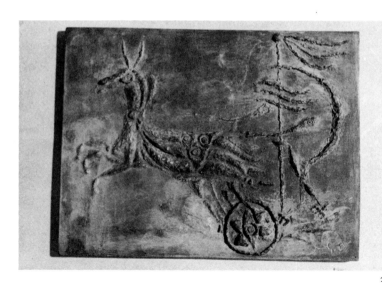

307

308

309. LA LOGE—OIL ON CANVAS—GEORGES ROUAULT—1938
—SIGNED—H. 15.2 cm. (6″)

"The Box" illustrates the "stained glass" and "enamel" effect identified with Rouault. Ex. Coll. Ambroise Vollard.

310. LE PORT—OIL ON CANVAS—MAURICE DE VLAMINCK—
1925—SIGNED—H. 71.1 cm. (28″)

"The Port" depicts Vlaminck's powerful, menacing sky over the turbulent sea at Le Havre. Ex. Coll. Jacob M. Goldschmidt.

312. LE PORTE DE PAIMPOL—WATERCOLOR—
PAUL SIGNAC—1927—SIGNED—H. 31.4 cm. (12⅜″)

Signac's watercolors retain the simple, fresh quality shown here in "The Port of Paimpol."

309

310

312

313. THE DONKEY OF SEELOW—BRONZE—RENEE SINTENIS
—1927—INITIALED—H. 80.3 cm. (31⅝")

The other cast of this charming animal is in the lobby of the
St. Louis Art Museum. A companion piece, "The Colt," was
formerly in the lobby of the Los Angeles County Museum of
Natural History. Because they both hold great appeal for children, the bronzes in the museums have been rubbed shiny by
their hands. Published: Hanna Kiel, *Renee Sintenis*, Berlin:
Rembrandt-Verlag, 1956.

314. HOMBRE CORRIENDO—OIL ON CANVAS—RUFINO
TAMAYO—1947—SIGNED—H. 99.8 cm. (38⅞")

Exhibited: Cincinnati Museum; National Museum, Mexico;
Museum of Modern Art, New York. Illustrated: Paul West-
heim, *El Arte de Tamayo*, Mexico City: Artes de Mexico, 1956.
Ex. Coll. Knoedler, Casa Misrachi.

315. YO LO VI—ETCHING—FRANCISCO JOSE DE GOYA—
BETWEEN 1811-21—SIGNED—H. 21.9 cm. (8⅝")

Goya's bitter, etched exposures of the foibles of men, with their
cryptic captions, express his caustic social comment. "I Saw It"
was published as pl. 44 in Goya's *Los Desastres de la Guerra*,
Madrid: R. Academia de Nobles Artes de San Fernando, 1863.

316. SACRED COW—DIRECT STEEL—JUAN NICKFORD—1949
—H. 20.2 cm. (8")

Here is an understandable and very powerful example of
welding-torch sculpture.

317. COMBAT—LITHOGRAPH—JOSEPH HIRSCH—1943—
SIGNED—H. 62.2 cm. (24½")

This lithograph won second prize in the Carnegie Exhibition
of 1947.

313

315

316

317

314

318. LUNA ROJA—PINK ONYX—MARINA NUNEZ DEL PRADO—1942—SIGNED—H. 47.2 cm. (18⅝″)

The "Red Moon" was acquired from the sculptress at her studio in La Paz, Bolivia, in 1957. It had previously been exhibited in many shows in the United States, Mexico, France, Spain, and South America, most recently at the Sao Paulo, Brazil showing of 1957.

319. TORSO FEMMINILE—BLACK MARBLE—ALBERTO VIANI —1945—H. 95.5 cm. (37⅝″)

This eminent Italian sculptor works in the tradition of Arp's biomorphic form, with a more classical reference, accomplishing an expression of an ancient feeling in an established modern idiom. Unfortunately he is not prolific, having produced only twenty-three marbles during the past nineteen years.

AWARDS. First Prize for Sculpture at First International Exhibition, Varese; First Prize, National Exhibition, Turin; First Prize, II International Biennale, Carrara; Gold Medal, First Biennale, Bari, etc.

EXHIBITED: Museum of Modern Art, New York; Royal Scottish Academy, Edinburgh; Venice Biennale; International Sculpture Exhibition, Antwerp; International Exhibition, Arnheim; Twentieth Century Sculpture Exhibition, Philadelphia, Chicago; Contemporary Italian Art, Stockholm; III International Biennale, Sao Paulo; Also: Rodin Museum, Paris; Australia; Japan; Carnegie Institute, Pittsburgh.

320. LE MARCHE A DIEPPE—WASH AND SEPIA DRAWING— CAMILE PISSARRO—CA. 1875—INITIALED—H. 12.2 cm. (4¾″)

The "Market of Dieppe" carries an inscription in Pissarro's handwriting. Ex. Coll. Ludovic-Rodo Pissarro.

321. THE TWO DUCKS—OIL ON WOOD PANEL—CARLO CANEVARI—1959—SIGNED—H. 26.8 cm. (10½″)

This young Florentine painter's work displays much humor. Its content is anecdotal.

322. CONSTELLATION—INK AND WATER COLOR ON PAPER—JOAN MIRO—1938—H. 43.2 cm. (17″)

This influential Spanish-born painter's work may be classified as halfway between the representational and the non-representational aspects of Surrealism. Its style is two dimensional Fauve-colorful, and graphic.

318

319

320

321

322

CONDENSED BIBLIOGRAPHY

GENERAL

Bacon, Edward. *Digging for History*. London: A. & C. Black, 1960.—Engrossing survey of today's archaeology.

Bibby, Geoffrey. *Testimony of the Spade*. New York: Knopf, 1956.—Learned approach through pre-history.

Breasted, James Henry. *Conquest of Civilization*. New York: Harper & Brothers, 1954.—Authoritative tour to end of ancient world.

Ceram, C. W. *Gods, Graves, and Scholars*. New York: Knopf, 1951.—Not best, but archaeology's greatest popularizer.

Coon, Carleton S. *Story of Man*. New York: Knopf, 1954.—Informed, readable, anthropological approach to homo sapiens.

Cottrell, Leonard (ed.). *The Concise Encyclopedia of Archaeology*. New York: Hawthorn, 1960.—Incommensurate but useful reference.

Encyclopedia of World Art. 15 vols. New York: McGraw-Hill, 1959-.—Exhaustive reference—pleasurable articles.

Hermann, Paul. *Conquest by Man*. New York: Harper, 1954.—Fascinating conglomerate of imaginative history and anecdotes.

Larousse Encyclopedia of Mythology. London: Batchworth Press Ltd., 1959.—Large gaps but comprehensive.

Lempriere, Jean L. *A Classical Dictionary*. (New ed. rev. with additions) New York: E. P. Dutton & Co., 1949.—Old standby, a requisite for reference.

Lissner, Ivan. *The Living Past*. New York: Putnam, 1957.—Delightful, rewarding reading of the ancient world.

Malraux, André. *The Voices of Silence*. New York: Doubleday, 1953.—Erudite theory and prescient observation of art.

Palmer, R. R. (ed.). *Atlas of World History*. Chicago: Rand McNally, 1957.—Necessity for geographical reference.

MESOPOTAMIA, THE LEVANT, AND EGYPT

Akurgal, Elrem. *The Art of the Hittites*. New York: H. N. Abrams, 1962.—Finally an all-inclusive coverage of this little published culture.

Cornfeld, G. (ed.). *Adam to Daniel*. New York: Macmillan, 1961.—Significant correlation between Biblical scholars and archaeology.

———. *Daniel to Paul*. New York: Macmillan, 1962.

Diehl, Charles. *Byzantium: Greatness and Decline*. New Brunswick, New Jersey: Rutgers University Press, 1957.—Skillful blend of art and complex history.

Dimand, Maurice S. *Handbook of Muhammadan Art*. New York: The Metropolitan Museum of Art, 1958.—Definitive work by a savant.

Encyclopedie photographique de l'art. Paris: Editions "Tel," 1935-49.—Magnificent compilation.

Ghirschman, Roman. *Persian Art*. New York: Golden Press, 1962.—A distillation of the writings by the masters of this field.

Hayes, William C. *The Scepter of Egypt*. 2 vols. New York: Harper in cooperation with The Metropolitan Museum of Art, 1953-1959.—Thesaurus in its bailiwick.

Lange, Kurt, and Hirmer, Max. *Egypt, Architecture, Sculpture, Painting in 3000 Years*. London: Phaidon Press, 1956.—History and art easily followed, using excellent plates.

Parrot, André. *Sumer*. London: Thames and Hudson, 1960.—Entrancing exploration of early Mesopotamia through its art.

———. *The Arts of Assyria*. New York: Golden Press, 1961.—Encompasses its sphere with generally ample text and sumptuous plates.

Pope, Arthur Upham (ed.). *A Survey of Persian Art*. London, New York: Oxford University Press, 1938.—His great work. Not light reading.

Rice, Tamara Talbot. *The Scythians*. New York: F. A. Praeger, 1957.—Comprehensive short view of a generally unrecognized culture.

Schmidt, Erich. *Persepolis*. 2 vols. Chicago: University of Chicago Press, 1953-57.—Tremendous publication, outstanding photographs of site.

GREECE, ROME, AND THE WEST

Block, Raymond. *Etruscan Art*. Greenwich, Conn.: New York Graphic Society, 1959.—A most articulate authority dwells on a fascinating civilization.

Brion, Marcel. *Pompeii and Herculaneum, the Glory and the Grief*. New York: Crown Publishers, 1960.—Buried cities yield their intriguing secrets.

Childe, Vere Gordon. *The Dawn of European Civilization*. New York: Knopf, 1957.—Major survey European pre-history; not light.

Gibbon, Edward. *The Decline and Fall of the Roman Empire*. D. M. Low abridgement. New York: Harcourt-Brace, 1960.—Great classic made palatable.

Hamilton, Edith. *The Greek Way*. New York: W. W. Norton & Company, Inc., 1930.—Our favorite; delightful reading leads to *Echo of Greece*.

MacKendrick, Paul. *The Mute Stones Speak*. New York: St. Martin's Press, 1960.—Italic field archaeology with anecdotal background.

Marinatos, Spyridon. *Crete and Mycenae*. New York: H. N. Abrams, 1960.—Beautifully illustrated monumental work.

Powell, Thomas George Eyre. *The Celts*. New York: F. A. Praeger, 1958.—Peregrinations and mores of people who probably were your ancestors.

Rawlinson, George. *Herodotus*. London: 1875-80.—Ironic humor, observations perpetuate first historian.

Richter, Gisella M. A. *A Handbook of Greek Art*. London: Phaidon Press, 1959.—Knowledgeable illumination of classical art.

Twining, Edward Francis. *A History of the Crown Jewels of Europe*. London: B. T. Batsford, 1960.—Follow history through jewels of rulers.

THE ORIENT

Cahill, James. *Chinese Painting*. Geneva: Skira, 1960.—Coherent, enlightening exposition on subtleties. Superior plates.

Coomaraswami, Ananda Kentish. *History of Indian and Indonesian Art*. New York: E. Weyhe, 1927.—Authoritative, pre-eminent.

Frankfort, Henri. *The Art and Architecture of the Ancient Orient*. Baltimore: Penguin Books, 1955.—Good textbook type of presentation.

Kelley, Charles Fabens. *Chinese Bronzes from Buckingham College*. Chicago: Chicago Art Institute, 1946.—Rewarding browsing.

Kempers, A. J. Bernet. *Ancient Indonesian Art*. Cambridge, Mass.: Harvard University Press, 1959.—Good delineation sans overelaborate commentary.

Kramrisch, Stella. *The Art of India*. New York: Phaidon Publishers, 1954.—Traditional but interesting coverage by text and picture.

Lee, Sherman E. *A History of Far Eastern Art*. New York: H. N. Abrams, 1964.—Heartily recommended. Comprehensive, filling a long-felt lack.

Michener, James Albert. *The Floating World*. New York: Random House, 1954.—Fine lay writer gambols in a field he obviously loves.

Wheeler, Sir Robert Eric Mortimer. *Early India and Pakistan: to Ashoka*. New York: F. A. Praeger, 1959.—Survey, tinged with pedantry, by top archaeologist.

Yashiro, Yukio. *2000 Years of Japanese Art*. ed. Peter C. Swann. New York: H. N. Abrams, 1958.—An alluringly beautiful book. Many plates.

Zimmer, Heinrich Robert. *The Art of Indian Asia, its Mythology and Transformations*. New York: Pantheon Books, 1955.—Work of great distinction, well illustrated.

OCEANIA AND THE PACIFIC BASIN

Christensen, Erwin Ottomar. *Primitive Art*. New York: Crowell, 1955.—Acceptable inclusion of other comparable cultures.

Linton, Ralph, and Wingert, Paul. *Arts of the South Seas*. New York: Museum of Modern Art, 1946.—Short but complete illustrated summary.

Wingert, Paul. *Art of the South Pacific Islands*. New York: Beechhurst Press, 1953.—An enchanting introduction through this book.

PRE-COLUMBIAN AMERICAS

Bennett, Wendell Clark. *Ancient Arts of the Andes*. New York: Museum of Modern Art, 1954.—Only concise and substantial exposition.

Bliss, Robert Woods. *Pre-Columbian Art*. Text and critical analyses by S. K. Lothrop, W. F. Foshang, Joy Mahler. New York: Phaidon, 1957.—Beautiful, uniformly great collection.

Covarrubias, Miguel. *The Eagle, the Jaguar, and the Serpent*. New York: Knopf, 1954.—By a talented man of omniverous interests.

Dockstader, Frederick J. *Indian Art in America*. Greenwich, Conn.: New York Graphic Society, 1960.—A scholar ennobles the red man.

Feuchtwanger, Franz. *The Art of Ancient Mexico*. London, New York: Thames and Hudson, 1954.—Outstanding compilation with well-chosen plates.

Kelemen, Pál. *Medieval American Art*. New York: Macmillan, 1956.—Exhaustively illustrated study of all cultures, techniques.

Morley, Sylvanus Griswold. *The Ancient Maya*. Rev. by George W. Brainerd. Palo Alto, Calif.: Stanford University Press, 1956.—Scholarly collaboration by two fine archaeologists.

Vaillant, George Clapp. *Aztecs of Mexico*. Garden City, New York: Doubleday, Doran & Company, Inc., 1941.—Remains the most definitive, although now partly outdated.

NEGRO AFRICA

Elisofon, Eliot. *The Sculpture of Africa*. New York: F. A. Praeger, 1958.—Fabulous photographs with entertaining, learned text.

Hamlyn, Paul. *Benin Art*. London: Batchworth Press Ltd., 1960—Pertinent plates on this specialty with concise comment.

Moorehead, Alan. *The White Nile*. New York: Harper, 1960.—Exciting adventure tales of the intrepid men who opened Africa.

Schmalenbach, Werner. *African Art*. New York: Macmillan, 1954.—Probably the most satisfactory general book on this area.

AND TO TODAY

Barr, Alfred H., Jr. (ed.). *Masters of Modern Art*. New York: Museum of Modern Art, 1954.—Fine contemporaneous panorama.

Berenson, Bernhard. *The Italian Painters of the Renaissance*. London: Phaidon Press, 1953.—Conclusion: great Italian art died circa 1600.

Canaday, John Edwin. *Mainstreams of Modern Art*. New York: Simon and Schuster, 1959.—Favorite critic's analysis; certainly opinionated.

Eliot, Alexander. *Three Hundred Years of American Painting*. New York: Time, Inc., 1957.—Comprehensive compilation. Satisfactory color reproductions.

Friedrich, Carl Joachim. *The Age of the Baroque, 1610-1660*. New York: Harper, 1952.—Best available on the age of flamboyance.

Gantner, Joseph, and Pobé, Marcel. *The Glory of Romanesque Art*. New York: Vanguard Press, 1956.—Treats of the rebirth of the XI and XII centuries.

Harvey, John Hooper. *The Gothic World, 1100-1600*. London, New York: B. T. Batsford, 1950.—Satisfactory scholarly standby, almost a textbook. Dull.

Janson, Horst Woldemar, and Janson, Dora Jane. *The Picture History of Painting, from Cave Painting to Modern Times*. New York: H. N. Abrams, 1957.—Requisite here, short history. Inoffensive, sequential.

Ketchum, Richard M. *The Horizon Book of the Renaissance*. New York: American Heritage Publishing Co., 1961.—Picture history of almost every facet of Renaissance life.

Marucci, Luisa, and Micheletti, Emma. *Medieval Painting*. New York: Viking Press, 1960.—Excellent despite garish reproductions, inclusive.

CATALOG DESIGN: Joseph Simon / Robert Weinstein

TYPES: 10 pt. Waverley, 24 pt. Hadriano open and Hadriano bold

PAPER: 80 lb. white Dorado Dull Text and 12 pt. white Lusterkote Cover

TYPOGRAPHY, BINDING AND PRINTING of a first edition of 5,000 copies by
Anderson, Ritchie and Simon, Los Angeles, California, 1971